Medical Humanities, Cultural Humility, and Social Justice

Perspectives in Health Humanities

UC Health Humanities Press publishes scholarship produced or reviewed under the auspices of the University of California Health Humanities Consortium, a multi-campus collaborative of faculty, students, and trainees in the humanities, medicine, and health sciences. Our series invites scholars from the humanities and health care professions to share narratives and analysis on health, healing, and the contexts of our beliefs and practices that impact biomedical inquiry.

General Editor

Brian Dolan, PhD, Professor, Department of Humanities and Social Sciences, University of California, San Francisco (UCSF)

Other Titles in this Series

www.UCHealthHumanitiesPress.com

This series is made possible by the generous support of the Dean of the School of Medicine at UCSF, the UCSF Library, and a Multicampus Research Program Grant from the University of California Office of the President. Grant ID MR-15-328363 and Grant ID M23PR5992.

Medical Humanities, Cultural Humility, and Social Justice

Edited by
Dalia Magaña,
Christina Lux, and
Ignacio López-Calvo

University of California
Center for Health Humanities
Department of Humanities and Social Sciences
UCSF (Box 0850)
490 Illinois Street, Floor 7
San Francisco, CA 94143-0850

Designed by Virtuoso Press

Library of Congress Control Number: 2023936350

ISBN: 978-1-7355423-6-2

Printed in USA

Contents

Introduction
Cultural Humility, Healthcare Equity, and Medical Humanities

Dalia Magaña, Christina Lux, and Ignacio López-Calvo
University of California, Merced

"*Muchos médicos nada más están escribe y escribe, y no te ven. No te ven como un paciente, te ven como un objeto.*" "Many doctors just write and write, and they don't see you. They don't see you as a patient, they see you as an object," explained Rosalba, a woman in her 40s. When Spanish speakers in rural California were asked about their experience during medical consultations with their providers, most expressed that they did not feel *heard* or *seen* (Magaña 2020). Rosalba's statement that her doctors do not see her as a patient but rather as an object encapsulates a shared frustration over rushed appointments with health practitioners who do not always acknowledge their presence (e.g., omit greetings), are not interested in getting to know the patient (e.g., omit small talk), or do not recognize patients as a knowledgeable party (e.g., do not listen to patients' perspectives and offer short explanations about diagnosis or procedures). These types of interactions violate the politeness norms that Latinxs with traditional ties to their culture practice. Such encounters can make people feel dehumanized, which may be one reason Latinxs underuse the healthcare system (Betancourt et al. 2011). Cultural competence (a knowledge base) and cultural humility (an approach to learning cultural knowledge) are critical in enhancing the medical experience for underserved communities and rebuilding their trust (*confianza*) in clinicians and the healthcare system. Through this volume, we propose that building on the concepts of cultural humility and competence, the medical humanities field has a role in helping improve the healthcare experience of *all*. Given the vast health-related disparities in the United States and their increase due to the COVID-19 pandemic, the need for innovative approaches to medical humanities is urgent. This collection brings together essays that either adopt a cultural humility approach or focus on social justice to shed new light on inequities within medical humanities.

The co-editors of this book live, work, and raise their families in a medically underserved area: Merced County, in California's Central Valley. Even as well-resourced and medically insured individuals, we experience challenges when trying to obtain primary health care for ourselves and our families. We have also witnessed the inequities that community members, such as Rosalba, face due to lack of insurance, undocumented status, lack of English proficiency, jobs that are not flexible enough to allow them to take time off for medical appointments, and/or the unaffordability of taking a day off from work.

Merced County, which constitutes a significant portion of the Central Valley, is vastly different from neighboring counties in the Bay Area (and much of the rest of California) given its lack of healthcare resources and the health disparities primarily afflicting communities of color. Latinxs, most of them of Mexican descent, comprise 60 percent of the county's population; it is otherwise 27 percent non-Hispanic white, 8 percent Asian (including a strong representation of Hmong people), 4 percent African American, and 2.5 percent American Indian (U.S. Census 2018). Most people in Merced County, 52.3 percent, speak a language other than English at home; 23 percent live in poverty, and only 13.8 percent have a college education (U.S. Census 2018). The county faces a severe provider shortage, along with a lack of access to adequate resources and consistent primary care, which contributes to the problematic healthcare experiences that patients like Rosalba encounter (Merced County Department of Public Health 2016).

The population has higher rates of obesity, diabetes, and asthma than the average in California. In addition, the COVID-19 pandemic's severe impact on Latinxs nationwide has been reflected in the county, as Merced's Latinxs, much like their counterparts in the rest of the United States, have a number of characteristics that increase their risk: they are disproportionately employed in high-risk fields during the pandemic (e.g., meatpacking, agricultural work, and other service jobs that require in-person employment); experience economic factors that make it more challenging to stay home from work; and have high rates of multi-generational households and high rates of conditions that increase the severity of disease (e.g., diabetes, HIV/AIDS) (American Public Health Association 2020; Krogstad, Gonzalez-Barrera, and Lopez 2020). A planned medical education program at the University of California, Merced offers hope in addressing these issues.

Alarmed by the healthcare inequities that plague our region, the Center for the Humanities at UC Merced decided to focus its research theme on medical humanities from 2018 to 2021. The series of lectures began before COVID-19 and continued through periods of quarantine and remote work, with the series ending just as we were able to come back to campus in person. Concurrently, UC Merced was grappling with questions about the future of medical education in the Central Valley of California. The reality of lack of access to medical care and the overburdening of the providers and structures we do have in place came into acute focus during the pandemic. Whereas from the academic fields of law, women's studies, and critical race and ethnic studies, many of our participants in these seminar discussions were already deeply familiar with intersectional approaches to research that examine structures of oppression, COVID-19 made the need for such approaches even more explicit and urgent (Laster Pirtle 2020; Laster Pirtle and Wright 2021).

In this sense, the timing of the medical humanities lecture series was both prescient and painfully relevant, as our colleagues were collectively grappling with such pressing questions. At times the subject matter felt almost too close – there is, after all, a reason we often see research studies and even historical novels emerge only many years after major traumatic events. However, because this series was ongoing at the onset of the pandemic, we were fortunate to have researchers and writers already engaged in conversations on the topic and willing to reflect on the events at hand. During this period, our community was in continual conversation about many of the overlapping consequences and realities that we were experiencing during COVID-19:

1. the importance of reflective, accurate, and timely communications
2. the danger of quick and reactive mass communications that disregarded science and played off of emotions like fear
3. a shift from an initial focus on how to remain productive to how to survive and adapt
4. a backlash to calls to resilience that neglected systemic inequities and that were focused on a drive to produce rather than fostering a culture of care
5. a renewed sense of how both cultural and professional humility are vital to our capacity to solve common problems and sustain communities

Such shifts have led us to reflect on the theoretical underpinnings of medical humanities as well as on how the field is evolving.

The medical humanities is an interdisciplinary field focused on understanding health in a way that offers key insights for patients, their loved ones, and healthcare practitioners who are devoted to improving care (Klugman 2017). It offers "nuanced and integrated perspectives on the fundamental aspects of illness, suffering, and healing" and encourages healthcare providers to examine their behavior and ways of thinking to improve patient care (Shapiro et al. 2009). It invites us to take seriously the human experience along with the biomedical approach to health care, thus offsetting the limitations of biological medicine (Viney, Callard, and Woods 2015). Increasingly gaining more attention at a global level, medical school curricula in the United States, Canada, and the United Kingdom often incorporate medical humanities.

Research shows that medical students who take medical humanities coursework exhibit greater empathy than a control group (Graham et al. 2016). A widespread example is how reading fiction helps medical providers consider other points of view, practice flexibility in their approach to understanding their patients' perspectives, and treat their patients with empathy (Graham et al. 2016). These changes can lead to more patient-centered care and better health outcomes for patients. For example, physicians' empathy was associated with more controlled hemoglobin levels among patients with diabetes (Hojat et al. 2011). Medical humanities also improve outcomes for practitioners: a US survey showed that exposing medical students to the humanities helped reduce their burnout (Mangione et al. 2018).

Narrative medicine is a subfield within medical humanities that has substantially impacted the delivery of health care. It emphasizes creating space during a medical consultation to listen to patients' illness testimonies in a holistic way. It encourages the provider to listen with an open mind, thus moving away from a paternalistic view of providers as the only knowledgeable party about illness and disease. It centers on patients' perspectives to help engage them in understanding the diagnosis and treatment.

Atkinson et al. (2015) argue that narrative medicine focuses too narrowly on the subjective experience of a patient, their survivorship, and a positive message, without critiquing the broader social and political circumstances that systematically affect the well-being of entire groups of people. For instance, this narrow view overlooks the collective illness experiences that affect marginalized groups. It ignores how the social determinants of health, meaning people's environments (i.e., where they live, learn, work, and play), affect their health. It is well documented that living in poverty creates stressors that, in turn, increase the chances of disease and decrease longevity (Wilkinson and Marmot 2003). Education levels are also known to predict health: those with higher levels of education lead healthier lives than those with less education (Marmot 2005). Likewise, underrepresented minorities have proportionately higher rates of poverty and lower rates of higher education. As Viney et al. propose, it is essential to account for the fact that "'race' and ethnicity, sexuality and gender, disability, technology and media, economics, and social and environmental inequalities are central to the production of medical knowledge and to the experience of health and illness" (2015, 3).

Communities of color in the United States experience disadvantages such as the lack of culturally competent providers (Cheng et al. 2018; Steinberg et al. 2016). The Association of American Medical Colleges describes three central domains for cultural competence: understanding people's healing traditions and systems; understanding their values, cultures, and beliefs; and having cross-cultural clinical skills to communicate effectively. Despite efforts to train medical professionals to offer culturally competent and patient-centered care, the United States faces a shortage of providers with the cultural competence to serve culturally diverse groups (Cheng et al. 2018; Steinberg et al. 2016). This inequity can create interpersonal conflicts in healthcare settings between patients and providers (Juckett 2013; Zamudio et al. 2017). For instance, if providers violate politeness norms that the cultural construct of *simpatía* (friendliness) dictates by not greeting Latinx patients, they may avoid future medical appointments as a result of perceiving that provider as rude or condescending. Demonstrating cultural knowledge facilitates more humane health care and can help patients feel empowered to claim agency during healthcare consultations (Magaña

2021). For these reasons, providers should be aware of healthcare-related cultural norms within the communities they serve.

Cultural competence should be viewed as an ongoing learning process instead of as expertise or a skill that can be mastered because cultural influences may change over time and space (Yeager and Bauer-Wu 2013). Given human complexity and heterogeneity, interventions meant to provide cultural competence should not include overgeneralizations about the behavior and values of certain social groups. Not only can people and communities vary, but such generalizations may promote harmful stereotypes. It may also promote a paternalistic approach to health care for patients with cultural perspectives on health that differ from mainstream biomedical approaches.

Scholars have proposed cultural humility as a necessary corrective to the idea that cultural competence is fixed knowledge. Cultural humility in the medical setting involves "a lifelong commitment to self-evaluation and critique, to redressing the power imbalances in the physician-patient dynamic, and to developing mutually beneficial and non-paternalistic partnerships with communities on behalf of individuals and defined populations" (Tervalon and Murray-García 1998, 123). It promotes a critical lens for provider-patient interactions through which providers are encouraged to be aware of their implicit biases and open to learning about others' values and beliefs. Cultural humility and cultural competence are synergistic, as they complement each other; whereas cultural humility is an *approach*, cultural competence is *knowledge*, which should be seen as a continuing process (Stubbe 2020). Both are crucial in offering patient-centered care.

Whereas medical humanities initially emerged as an applied training tool in medical schools with a primary focus on praxis and pedagogy, among humanists, the focus has often shifted to how our humanistic disciplines engage with medical science, history, and practice, thus having less of an applied nature. This applied nature of medical humanities in medical schools and the emerging resistance to such curricula among some students, as documented by Shapiro et al. (2009), should be a cause for concern among both humanists and medical schools. If the field becomes overly didactic and instrumental, an add-on instead of continually engaging all scholars in an ongoing conversation, we may create doctors who resent or push back on the value of the medical humanities overall or who solidify a divide between disciplines where we are seeking to create connection. Pederson (2010), for example, describes the pitfall of the persistent dichotomy between natural and human sciences in medical education, exposing how it can negatively affect the cultivation of empathy in medical training. This is where stepping back to consider broader theoretical concerns may be useful in framing the medical humanities in more innovative ways.

Perhaps one of the most exciting ideas to emerge in medical humanities in the past decade is Viney et al.'s (2015) concept of "entanglement," which focuses on the potential of a "critical" medical humanities. Fitzgerald and Callard (2016) expand on the concept, explaining how previous models of integration between humanities and medicine were conservative and problematic. Instead, they encourage medical humanities practitioners and scholars to attend to the *differences* between humanities and medicine, recognizing that "medicine and life itself are constituted precisely through relations and through practices of bordering, cutting and exchange through which those relations come to matter." They add that "[t]here is neither an additive nor an integrative 'human' at the heart of the medical humanities; there are, rather, animacies, vitalities and pathologies, which flow across different practices and preoccupations that then come to be ascribed to the 'humanities' and the 'biosciences'" (2016, 44-45).

If we further build upon the concept of entanglement to frame the essays in this volume, we may examine how the emphasis on relation and its consequent mutual effects and obligations can assist us with approaches not only to dismantle structural inequities, but also to explore associated frameworks, images, and metaphors that can guide us in this process. We would like to paint a picture of interdependence for our readers that may be useful in our ongoing framing of medical humanities. We believe that the cultivation of associated metaphors and images will help us to unveil the potential of this field with each new articulation.

Metaphors that initially seem distant from our immediate fields can be useful in reframing problems; indeed, taking psychological distance has enhanced problem-solving creativity (Jia, Hirt, and Karpen 2009). The metaphor we would like to share with you comes from environmental studies and is related to how plants in the Sahel region in Africa help each other survive drought. During a state of emergency for California due to drought (which had many health-related impacts as entire communities lost access to water), our colleague Teamrat Ghezzehei, an environmental scientist, delivered the talk "Securing Agricultural Productivity using Native Woody Shrubs in the Peanut Basin, Senegal" with collaborator Nate Bogie during one of our Center for the Humanities' working groups on African and African Diaspora Studies. Ghezzehei shared the example of how environmental scientists approached a local practice in Senegal, whereby farmers planted crops alongside native shrubs to enhance crop productivity and food production. This unique system helps with water availability because when native woody shrubs grow near crops, their deep roots bring water to the level where the crops can access it and survive during drought periods. The story reflects how important it is for scientists to listen to local or indigenous knowledge to drive inquiry, which requires approaching the problem from a position of cultural and professional humility. It calls on us to remember the value of taking the time to listen and observe, of practicing cultural humility by remaining open to one's own gaps in professional knowledge instead of just focusing on demonstrating competence. This image of mutual effects and obligations drawn from environmental studies may allow us to envision how entanglement in the medical humanities can function. It calls on us to presume inherent interconnectedness and potential mutual benefits, as well as to be willing to risk trying a counterintuitive approach to solve problems.

In this case, if farmers had assumed that the plants were always competing for water, they would not have planted crops alongside shrubs and would have missed a potentially life-saving solution for many communities. Similarly, entanglement as a theoretical framework for medical humanities calls on us to operate from a position that does not require a defensive, territorial disciplinary posture, or from an assumption that we are always competing for limited resources (time, money, or expertise) and that our proximity or relation may make us "lose out" if we are not careful. It helps us to be open to new insights from many perspectives that may lead to innovation and improvement in medical care and health outcomes, while also striving toward social justice, in our example, by learning from and respecting local indigenous knowledge.

Similarly, community-engaged scholarship, an approach that has been fostered at the University of California, Merced, guides researchers to create collaborative partnerships with more effective and mutually beneficial approaches (Wallerstein et al. 2017). For example, a collaboration between researchers and a non-profit organization can build an infrastructure where research participants can continue obtaining resources from the organization long after the project is over. In this sense, community-engaged scholarship empowers communities so that they can be agents of change even after a research project is completed (Manzo et al. 2020).

Incorporating approaches used in community-engaged research into medical humanities studies can expand the possibilities of centering people of color's voices to examine the challenges they experience in the healthcare system and to uncover their individual and collective experiences in seeking and obtaining treatment. For example, Dalia Magaña is conducting a study on how Latinas in the Central Valley use metaphors in their breast cancer narratives to express their cultural values. It explores how their cultural belief systems influence how rural Latinas cope with a breast cancer diagnosis and treatment through a partnership with Healthy House, a nonprofit organization in Merced that offers interpretation services and trains medical residents on cultural competence.

Healthy House and the UC Merced researchers believe that language awareness, such as recognizing metaphors related to cancer, is critical in improving healthcare communication and cultural competence. However, research thus far has focused on English-language metaphors. For many English speakers in the United States, cancer treatment is war, as in "my *fight* against cancer," "I have a good chance of *beating* cancer," and "I hope to *win* this *battle*." English speakers use war metaphors in cancer narratives to form solidarity against the disease, and oncologists also use them to encourage patients. However, this is not as common among rural Latinas, who use metaphors more connected to spirituality, family, and community. For example, participants in Magaña's study said things like, "I *walk through* this disease with family and God by my *side*." Instead of war metaphors, they reference a more collective approach to getting through the disease. We contend that familiarity with these cultural differences is vital for understanding disease from patients' perspectives, thus working toward effective healthcare communication and creating an inclusive environment. It is alienating when the dominant cultural views of health, such as those where cancer is seen as a battle, are imposed onto minoritized groups, since the differences in metaphor choices are grounded in their cultural contexts. People affected by healthcare inequities are the experts on these issues; research must identify their knowledge and give them a voice to improve advocacy and community interventions (Deeb-Sossa 2019).

This volume moves away from the traditional narrow focus of medical humanities by engaging with issues beyond the medical encounter, connecting, instead, health care, wellbeing, and illness more widely to communities, specifically those socially and/or politically marginalized. It thus includes essays based on community-engaged scholarship to understand the intersubjective experiences of communities of color in health care, the strengths of community collaborations in addressing health epidemics, and the best approaches to support the health and well-being of marginalized groups. It includes work from scholars across various disciplines (ethnomusicology, linguistics, literature, psychology), community advocates, and healthcare providers to offer a variety of cases illustrating the value of medical humanities. Many chapters take a critical stance in producing medical humanities scholarship. For instance, Yvette G. Flores's chapter proposes a decolonial strategy to understand mental health among Latinxs during the pandemic, the barriers afflicting this group, and solutions rooted in Latinx culture.

This volume acknowledges the experiences of minoritized groups, including people with disabilities and debilitating health concerns, recognizing them as knowledge producers in health care, illness, and diseases. Thus, several chapters are devoted to centering the health narratives of people with disabilities (autism, aphasia) and women with endometriosis (a debilitating condition that is often misunderstood and misdiagnosed). The essays' styles are as varied as their content; this is a deliberate decision to practice a crucial lesson from the medical humanities about exercising openness and acceptance when considering a range of points of view.

A unifying factor is that every contribution to this volume addresses social justice. Broadly speaking, then, the concerns of this volume include "equitable distribution of resources, respect for human rights, equitable access to opportunities, political representation, cultural respect, and social recognition" (Avineri et al. 2019, 3). Working toward social justice in healthcare institutions means expanding access to prevent people from being excluded due to minoritized status, including disability, gender, race, ethnicity, religion, social class, language, and literacy levels. It also means demonstrating professional and cultural humility in working with patients and communities toward better health outcomes.

As the chapters in this volume illustrate, the medical humanities have a role in bringing down the barriers that prevent marginalized groups from having equitable access to health care, such as language and cultural barriers. They also demonstrate the role of health literacy in promoting equity in health care. We feature reports on health issues and wellbeing of Black and Latinx groups, who have greater mistrust of the healthcare system than whites, in part due to systemic racism and historic abuse in clinical settings (e.g., unethical research, medical experimentation). For instance, one of the essays describes the role of community-engaged research as an approach to rebuilding trust with Black communities and understanding their experiences with outbreaks such as COVID-19. The essays point out health issues that are often overlooked or that afflict minoritized groups and offer wisdom on the best approaches toward solutions to address them.

The Book's Organization

The first four essays in this volume focus on alternative approaches to reframing disabilities, understanding debilitating illnesses, and the role of narratives and health literacy in promoting patient-centeredness and equity in health care. The remaining turn to issues of health inequities afflicting underrepresented minoritized groups in sleep deprivation, mental health, and infectious diseases. Collectively, the essays offer lessons on how cultural competence, cultural humility, and social justice can serve as guiding points to explore new possibilities in engaging with medical humanities.

Drawing from two decades of research on music and autism, Michael B. Bakan and Graeme Gibson's chapter approaches the medical humanities from the perspective of ethnomusicology and re-presentational ethnography.

This case study links together different domains of human experience, such as autism, neurodiversity, personhood, and melomania to "re-present" the lived experience of an autistic person via ethnomusicology through dialogue, respect, and listening. The chapter reveals how a Canadian young man, who sees his identity and worldview in relation to his life with autism, makes, experiences, and finds meaning in music. It also provides his views on different types of music, his experience with music teachers and therapists, the support of his family, as well as his understanding of autism and how autistic minds work.

Continuing to address efforts to privilege the patient's perspective, Brian Dolan explores, in his chapter, the connections between autobiographical narrative language and self-identity, focusing on how life memories are articulated through *narrative*. As he explains, life history and identity are formed through the logical ordering and interpretation of stories that we tell ourselves about memories of past autobiographical events. However, this story does not need to be spoken aloud; it can be related, instead, through self-talk and internal monologue. But what happens when language is taken away, when disorders affect the ability to recall memories, construct stories, dream, and create internal monologue? Within the context of language as the key element to understanding oneself and making meaning in life, Dolan examines what aphasia and other neurological disorders can tell us about philosophical conceptions of self, contextualizing it within medical efforts to "reconnect" patients to their world through language usage. The chapter also looks at how aphasia presents a challenge to clinical rehabilitation. In his own words, "Because of the privilege we place upon language as a tool to define ourselves, we run the risk of mishandling that tool."

The chapter by Mariana Pascual studies how Chilean women use language to construct negative and positive affect in sharing their experiences with endometriosis. This medical condition, which afflicts about 1 in 10 women, causes debilitating pain and/or infertility yet is often misdiagnosed.

The study uses discourse analysis to uncover how Chilean women express meaning and evaluate their experiences with endometriosis across two different genres: social media comments and narratives collected through semi-structured interviews. Using quantitative and qualitative analysis, it concludes that the normalization of menstrual suffering and female pain in general, together with the cultural mistrust of women's emotions, contribute to deteriorating patients' quality of life. Furthermore, these misconceptions, along with a lack of concern and sympathy, prevent timely diagnoses. The chapter makes a strong case for the need to understand endometriosis from the patient perspective to further improve their quality of care and support.

Yu-Han Chao's chapter addresses the potential of Advance Health Care Directives and end-of-life considerations to improve the quality of life and to respect the wishes of patients and their loved ones. As Chao explains, patients' quality of life and experience can be improved by specifying in advance their preferences regarding intubation, cardiopulmonary resuscitation, artificial nutrition, and other medical interventions with which their relatives, and the general public, are not usually familiar. While the first part of the essay narrates Chao's personal experience as a case study, the second part focuses on her experiences as an ICU nurse during the COVID-19 pandemic, when relatives with limited health literacy had no alternative but to make healthcare decisions for patients without any knowledge of their wishes. The chapter closes by focusing on a typical Advance Health Care Directive Form and treatment options (process, risks, alternatives, and benefits) to prevent patients from being treated against their will and receiving the treatment they choose instead.

Ithar Hassaballa and Ruaa Hassaballa-Muhammad combine their vast global experience in community-based participatory research to understand and address gaps in public health and development. Their essay, "Successful Global Health Partnerships Between Kansas and Congo: Addressing Capacity Building Needs, Ebola, and COVID-19," sheds light on how they use their collective experience in working toward health equity, specifically in engaging Black communities affected by infectious disease outbreaks. They report on their collaborative work between the World Health Organization's (WHO) Regional Office for Africa and the WHO's Collaborating Center at the University of Kansas, sharing their approach to creating resources and capacity for building healthy communities. They evaluate and contrast both the Ebola and COVID-19 response efforts globally, addressing health inequities related to social determinants of health. The authors offer lessons learned related to their global health engagements as guidance for others conducting community-based scholarship.

Yvette Flores is a leading scholar in Latinx mental health, an educator, and a community clinical psychologist with over thirty years of experience. Her essay offers new insights into the factors driving the disproportionate rates of COVID-19 complications and deaths among Latinx groups. After presenting a socio-historical context of Latinxs in the United States, the essay provides an overview of the factors that led to disproportionate rates of depression, suicidal thoughts, and substance abuse during the pandemic. For instance, Flores explains why even though Latinxs experience more stress over work, food, and housing insecurity than whites, they have lower levels of mental health utilization. Factors include lower rates of medical insurance, lack of Spanish-speaking providers, and lack of cultural competence among practitioners. Stressors among Latinxs are amplified by racism, from everyday microaggressions to the images reproduced in the media of "*bad hombres*" and "Latinas having anchor babies." Flores's essay offers a case study of how she and her colleagues in UC Davis's Chicana/o Studies program approached teaching during the pandemic and supported their majority Latinx students. In her courses, she guides students to examine gender roles and how some Latinx cultural constructs may conflict with what is needed to cope with pandemic-related stressors: self-care. Connecting theory to students' experiences offers a pedagogical model that benefits students' educational experience and well-being. She concludes by providing her insight for those of us who are educators about the lessons the pandemic has taught us.

Works Cited

American Public Health Association. 2020. "AHPA leader calls for greater access to COVID-19 resources for Hispanics." Accessed April 2021. https://www.apha.org/news-and-media/news-releases/apha-news-releases/2020/hispanics-and-covid-19.

Atkinson, Sarah, Bethan Evans, Angela Woods, and Robin Kearns. 2015. "'The Medical' and 'Health' in a Critical Medical Humanities." *Journal of Medical Humanities* 36, no. 1: 71-81. doi: 10.1007/s10912-014-9314-4.

Avineri, Netta, Laura R. Graham, Eric J. Johnson, Robin Conley Riner, and Jonathan Rosa. ed. 2019. *Language and Social Justice in Practice*. New York: Routledge.

Betancourt, Hector, Patricia M. Flynn, and Sarah R. Ormseth. 2011. "Healthcare mistreatment and continuity of cancer screening among Latino and Anglo American women in Southern California." *Women & Health* 51, no. 1: 1-24.

Cheng, Hsiu-Lan, Anna Lopez, Jamey L. Rislin, Helen Youngju Kim, Joshua Turner, Heather Terhorst-Miller, Jessica Lopez-Harder, and Chu Hui Cha. 2018. "Latino/Hispanic Community Adults' Healthcare Experience in a New Mexico Borderland Region." *Journal of Health Disparities Research and Practice* 11, no. 4, article 5. https://digitalscholarship.unlv.edu/jhdrp/vol11/iss4/5.

Deeb-Sossa, Natalia. ed. 2019. *Community-Based Participatory Research: Testimonios from Chicana/o Studies*. Tucson: University of Arizona Press.

Dong, Jie. 2021. "Language and globalization revisited: Life from the periphery in COVID-19." *International Journal of the Sociology of Language*, no. 267-268: 105-110. https://doi.org/10.1515/ijsl-2020-0086.

Eyster, Harold N., Terre Satterfield, and Kai M.A. Chan. 2022. "Why People Do What They Do: An Interdisciplinary Synthesis of Human Action Theories." *Annual Review of Environment and Resources* 47. https://doi.org/10.1146/annurev-environ-020422-125351.

Fitzgerald, Des and Felicity Callard. 2016. "Entangling the Medical Humanities." In *The Edinburgh Companion to the Critical Medical Humanities*, edited by Anne Whitehead and Angela Woods, 35-49. Edinburgh: Edinburgh University Press.

Graham, Jeremy, Lauren M. Benson, Judy Swanson, Darryl Potyk, Kenn Daratha, and Ken Roberts. 2016. "Medical Humanities Coursework Is Associated with Greater Measured Empathy in Medical Students." *The American Journal of Medicine* 129, no.12: 1334-1337.

Hojat, Mohammadreza, Daniel Z. Louis, Fred W. Markham, Richard Wender, Carol Rabinowitz, and Joseph S. Gonnella. 2011. "Physicians' empathy and clinical outcomes for diabetic patients." *Academic medicine: journal of the Association of American Medical Colleges* 86, no.3: 359–364. https://doi.org/10.1097/ACM.0b013e3182086fe1.

Juckett, Gregory. 2013. "Caring for Latino patients." *American Family Physician* 87, no.1: 48–54.

Jia, Lile, Edward R. Hirt, and Samuel C. Karpen. 2009. "Lessons from a Faraway Land: The Effect of Spatial Distance on Creative Cognition." *Journal of Experimental Social Psychology* 45, no. 5: 1127-1131.

Klugman, Craig M. 2017. "How Health Humanities Will Save the Life of the Humanities." *The Journal of Medical Humanities* 38, no. 4: 419-430.

Krogstad, Jens Manuel, Ana Gonzalez-Barrera, and Mark Hugo Lopez. 2020. "Hispanics more likely than Americans overall to see coronavirus as a major threat to health and finances." Pew Research Center. Accessed April 20, 2021.https://www.pewresearch.org/fact-tank/2020/03/24/hispanics-more-likely-than-americans-overall-to-see-coronavirus-as-a-major-threat-to-health-and-finances/.

Laster Pirtle, Whitney N. 2020. "Racial Capitalism: A Fundamental Cause of Novel Coronavirus (COVID-19) Pandemic Inequities in the United States." *Health Education & Behavior* 47, no. 4: 504-508.

Laster Pirtle, Whitney N., and Tashelle Wright. 2021. "Structural Gendered Racism Revealed in Pandemic Times: Intersectional Approaches to Understanding Race and Gender Health Inequities in COVID-19." *Gender & Society* 35, no. 2: 168-179.

Magaña, Dalia. 2020. "Local Voices on Healthcare Communication Issues and Insights on Latino Cultural Constructs." *Hispanic Journal of Behavioral Sciences* 42, no. 3: 300–323.

Magaña, Dalia. 2021. *Building confianza: Empowering Latinos/as through transcultural health care communication.* The Ohio State University Press.

Mangione, Salvatore, Chayan Chakraborti, Giuseppe Staltari, Rebecca Harrison, Allan R. Tunkel, Kevin T. Liou, Elizabeth Cerceo, Megan Voeller, Wendy L. Bedwell, Keaton Fletcher, and Marc J. Kahn. 2018. "Medical Students' Exposure to the Humanities Correlates with Positive Personal Qualities and Reduced Burnout: A Multi-Institutional U.S. Survey." *Journal of General Internal Medicine* 33, no. 5: 628–634.

Manzo, Rosa D., Lisceth Brazil-Cruz, Yvette G. Flores, and Hector Rivera-Lopez. 2020. *Cultura y Corazón: A Decolonial Methodology for Community Engaged Research.* Tucson: The University of Arizona Press.

Marmot, Michael. 2005. *Status Syndrome: How Your Social Standing Directly*

Affects Your Health. London: Bloomsbury Publishing.

Merced County Department of Public Health. 2016. Merced County: 2016 Community Health Assessment. Accessed June 2022. https:// www.countyofmerced.com/DocumentCenter/View/12213/CHA-FINAL---V1?bidId=.

Pedersen, Reidar. 2010. "Empathy development in medical education - A critical review." *Medical Teacher* 32, no. 7: 593-600.

Shapiro, Johanna, Jack Coulehan, Delese Wear, and Martha Montello. 2009. "Medical Humanities and Their Discontents: Definitions, Critiques, and Implications." *Academic Medicine* 84, no. 2: 192-198.

Steinberg, Emma M., Doris Valenzuela-Araujo, Joseph S. Zickafoose, Edith Keiffer, and Lisa Ross Decamp. 2016. "The "Battle" of Managing Language Barriers in Health Care." *Clinical Pediatrics* 55, no. 14: 1318–1327. https://doi.org/10.1177/0009922816629760.

Stubbe, Dorothy E. 2020. "Practicing Cultural Competence and Cultural Humility in the Care of Diverse Patients." *Focus* 18, no. 1: 49-51.

Tervalon, Melanie, and Jann Murray-García. 1998. "Cultural Humility Versus Cultural Competence: A Critical Distinction in Defining Physician Training Outcomes in Multicultural Education." *Journal of Health Care for the Poor and Underserved* 9, no. 2: 117-125.

U.S. Census Bureau. 2018. Quickfacts. Accessed May 2021. https://www. census.gov/quickfacts/fact/table/mercedcountycalifornia,mercedcityc alifornia,US/PST045218.

Viney, William, Felicity Callard, and Angela Woods. 2015. "Critical medical humanities: embracing entanglement, taking risks." *Medical Humanities* 41, no. 1: 2-7.

Wallerstein, Nina, Bonnie Duran, John Oetzel, and Meredith Minkler. 2017. *Community-Based Participatory Research for Health: Advancing Social and Health Equity*. 3rd ed. San Francisco: Jossey-Bass (A Wiley Brand).

Wilkinson, Richard G., and Michael Marmot. 2003. *Social determinants of health: The solid facts.* World Health Organization.

Yeager, Katherine A. and Susan Bauer-Wu. 2013. "Cultural humility: Essential foundation for clinical researchers." *Applied Nursing* 26 no. 4: 1-12.

Zamudio, Cindy D., Gabriela Sanchez, Andrea Altschuler, and Richard W. Grant. 2017. "Influence of Language and Culture in the Primary Care of Spanish-Speaking Latino Adults with Poorly Controlled Diabetes: A Qualitative Study." *Ethnicity & Disease* 27, no. 4: 379–386. https://doi.org/10.18865/ed.27.4.379.

1

Music, Autism, and Neurodiversity in Re-presentational Perspective

Michael B. Bakan, *Florida State University*
Graeme Gibson

Abstract:

How do autistic people make, experience, and find meaning in music, and why does it matter to them that they do? These are the fundamental questions at issue in this chapter, which centers on the musical life of Graeme Gibson, a multi-instrumentalist, composer, instrument builder and collector, and online world music instrument museum curator based in Vancouver, Canada. Graeme is on the autism spectrum and regards that identity as integral to the ways in which he both engages with music and defines his worldview in relation to it. The chapter unfolds mainly through dialogue between Graeme and ethnomusicologist Michael Bakan. Methodologically, it rests on an approach of re-presentational ethnography, which contrasts with its more established counterpart, representational ethnography. In the frame of re-presentational ethnography, dialogues between the person who conducts the research and the person about whom the research is conducted are not starting points for the types of description, analysis, and interpretation that usually foster the creation of ethnographic texts. Rather, these conversations *are* the text, with the direct contributions of the researcher being limited, first, to what they contributed *to* the conversation in the role of dialogue partner, and second, to the making of a layer of narration—and as light a layer as possible—provided to ensure that the core dialogue text comes through with sufficient clarity and cohesiveness to make it engaging and readily understandable. Through this re-presentational lens, we are invited into a dialogical space in which Graeme expresses, in his own words, his views on a wide range of topics and issues, including the subtleties of Indian raga, the experience of working with renowned music teachers and therapists, the role of family in autism support networks, and ultimately the question of what autism is and how autistic minds work.

This chapter approaches the relationship between life, music, autism, and neurodiversity from an ethnomusicological perspective, with ethnomusicology here defined as "the study of how people make and experience music, and of why it matters to them that they do" (Bakan 2015, 117). The chapter focuses on the life, music, scholarship, and philosophical perspectives of Graeme Gibson, a multi-instrumentalist, composer, instrument builder, and online instrument museum curator in his mid-forties who is based in Vancouver, Canada. Graeme is on the autism spectrum, having been diagnosed with an autism spectrum condition, or ASC (our preferred terminology over "autism spectrum disorder," or ASD – see Fein and Rios 2018), at the age of two.

Graeme's interlocutor throughout the chapter is Michael Bakan, an ethnomusicologist and musician who has been making music, talking about music, and doing ethnomusicology with autistic people for some two decades, including through publications (Bakan 2016, Bakan 2018, Bakan et al. 2018, Bakan et al. 2021, Nitzberg and Bakan 2019), conference presentations, and musical performances.[1] Deborah Gibson, Graeme's

1. Significant portions of this chapter were originally published in *Speaking for Ourselves: Conversations on Life, Music, and Autism*, by Michael B. Bakan and ten co-authors (Bakan et al. 2018), as well as in the paperback version of that same work, *Music and Autism: Speaking for Ourselves* (2021), and have been reproduced by permission of Oxford University Press [https://global.oup.com/academic/product/speaking-for-ourselves-9780190855833?cc=us&lang=en&].

mother, was also an active participant in the dialogue sessions that shaped this work, and her words and ideas, along with Graeme's and Michael's, are integral to what follows.

The core of the chapter is to be found in its transcription-based narrative re-presentations of a series of online dialogues that took place between the two co-authors (joined by Deborah in some instances) during the summer of 2014. These conversations themselves, as well as the theoretical and methodological foundations of the chapter's dialogue-based, music experience-centered, re-presentational approach, draw extensively from earlier publications (Bakan 2019, Bakan et al. 2018, Bakan et al. 2021).

Re-presentational ethnography, a concept which, to the best of our knowledge, was first introduced in print by Bakan in a colloquy published several years ago (Bakan 2016), differs substantially from the various forms of representational ethnography that have long been the stock in trade for fields like ethnomusicology and cultural anthropology. In re-presentational ethnography, the conversation itself—be that in the form of a live face-to-face interview, a Zoom call, an online chat using text messaging, or even an interactive musical performance—is not a starting point for the types of description, analysis, and interpretation that usually foster the creation of ethnographic texts. Rather, these conversations *are* the text, with the direct contributions of the researcher (in this case, Bakan) being limited, first, to what they contributed *to* the conversation in the role of dialogue partner, and second, to the making of a layer of narration—and as light a layer as possible—provided to ensure that the core dialogue text comes through with sufficient clarity and cohesiveness to make it engaging and readily understandable; in short, the result of dialogue-based, re-presentational ethnography is the creation of texts *of* conversations rather than texts based on conversations.

As the anthropologist and autism scholar Laura Sterponi has written, in this work "Ethnographic 'subjects' who would traditionally be merely *represented*, spoken about in a conventional scholarly paper on autism spectrum conditions, are given equal or perhaps even greater status and authoritativeness than [the researcher/scholar who would conventionally be credited as] the 'official author'" (Sterponi 2015). Here, the recognized, indisputable "authoritativeness" of Graeme Gibson as the world's leading expert on himself—musically, intellectually, and otherwise—finds representation in an equal sharing of authorial credit with Bakan. (It should be noted that Graeme elected to take second-author rather than first-author credit, and also that Deborah has chosen not to be credited as a co-author of this chapter).

In many respects, the methods and theoretical bases underlying re-presentational ethnography overlap considerably with those of other scholarly and literary genres, including interviews published in magazines and on websites, contemporary author interviews published by literary scholars, and oral histories published by historians and folklorists. The fundamental differences between these other genres and the genre of re-presentational ethnography advanced here have to do with issues of epistemology, training, and orientation, to which we now turn attention.

Despite its distinct identity relative to various related forms of representational ethnography, re-presentational ethnography remains epistemologically tied to the formative priorities, values, and conceptual moorings of the ethnographic project writ large, whether within frames of cultural anthropology or adjacent disciplines such as ethnomusicology. The ethnographic goals and objectives of anthropologists and ethnomusicologists differ significantly from those of historians or folklorists who engage in oral history projects, as well as from those of journalists, literary scholars, and others who rely on interview-based methods in their work to a significant degree. As a result, the transformation of their interview/conversation-generated data into written-word publications is markedly different in outcome.

Inextricable from this level of difference is another one stemming from the fact that oral historians and folklorists, let alone journalists and literary scholars, experience very different courses of professional training than their anthropologist/ethnomusicologist counterparts. In all cases, the give-and-take of conversational exchange and its "translation" into published writings—whether framed in terms of dialogues, interviews, or other modes of communicative interaction—might be reasonably said to encompass a significant component of "re-presentation." The form and substance of that re-presentation, however, varies greatly from one genre to another, whether that variance is gauged by the types of questions that are asked, the parameters of the interactive engagement itself, or the larger epistemological frames of knowledge production and interpretation that both prefigure the conversational encounter in the first place and direct what is done *with* the "data" generated by that conversation in its aftermath. On all of these levels, re-presentational ethnography of the type modeled in this chapter occupies a unique position within the larger universe of dialogic/interview-centered genres of scholarship. We are confident that the discursive space created in what follows will model and provide evidence in support of this claim.

Graeme Gibson

November 14, 2013. Michael Bakan is at the Society for Ethnomusicology conference in Indianapolis and encounters an old friend: the composer, instrument collector, multi-instrumentalist, and ethnomusicologist Randy Raine-Reusch. Michael and Randy have not seen each other in many years. They strike up a conversation, and the subject quickly turns to music and autism. Randy tells Michael that he has been following his work, which is especially interesting to Randy because he has an autistic student, Graeme Gibson, whom he has been teaching for over twenty years. Graeme and Randy both live in Vancouver, where Michael also grew up. Randy tells

Michael that Graeme was diagnosed with "classic autism" as a young child. From a very early age, he showed a passionate interest in music and musical instruments. Since then, he has amassed a large and diverse instrument collection, which he now curates and shares with the world via his digital instrument museum: museumofworldmusic.com (Gibson, G., n.d.). Graeme plays most of the many instruments he owns. He taught himself to play a number of them and studied the others with either Randy or his other long-standing teacher, the Peruvian-Canadian musician René Hugo Sánchez.

Graeme is now in his mid-thirties, Randy reports to Michael during their 2013 chat, adding that Graeme has been living on his own for several years, though he maintains a very close relationship with his parents, Deborah and Bill. Randy describes Deborah and Bill as "really nice folks" who have avidly supported Graeme's musical pursuits throughout his life. Moreover, he informs Michael that Deborah's Ph.D. dissertation was on autism and early childhood language development, with Graeme as her principal case study (Gibson, D. 2011).

Nothing more is said about Bill at the time, though Michael will later learn that Graeme's father is the iconic science fiction novelist William Gibson, the author of *Neuromancer* (1984) and other international bestsellers, and the writer reported to have coined the term "cyberpunk." The more Randy tells Michael about Graeme, the more excited Michael becomes about the prospect of interviewing Graeme for his then-in-progress book project, which will come to fruition about five years later as *Speaking for Ourselves* (Bakan et al. 2018).

"He's into some pretty amazing things," Randy says of Graeme with pride: composing original pieces, recording in his home studio, building musical instruments, and doing wildlife photography and volunteer work as a data-entry specialist at both a museum and a local radio station. "You should get in touch with him. Go through his mom. That's your best bet. Here's her contact information."

Randy takes out one of his business cards, writes Deborah's email address on the back, and hands it to Michael.

"Great seeing you, Mike!"

Michael emails Deborah as soon as he is back home in Tallahassee, Florida. He shares some information about himself and the book project, and asks Deborah whether she thinks Graeme might be interested in participating. She encourages him to send Graeme some questions to answer via email, which he does promptly. Graeme eventually gets back to Michael with a thoughtful email response on June 9, 2014.

"My best answer to give to Dr. Michael Bakan is that I play a range of different stringed instruments, particularly lutes, and some zithers," Graeme's email begins. "My specialty[,] though[,] is stringed instruments. I may play whatever it is I feel like, which the particular instrument may convey the sound of the mood. Or I may play something I learn from my music teachers, Randy Raine-Reusch, who you may know, and my second teacher, Rene Hugo Sanchez, who is from Peru. As to my personal relationships with my teachers, I share both interests, and in turn, I continue to learn a great deal from them. I currently study with my teacher Rene Hugo Sanchez while Randy and his wife, Mei Han, are in Ohio. I'm also involved in documenting the repertoire I learn by recording or writing it down in tablature or staff notation on my computer. In learning music, I'm a visual learner; instructions I do learn from listening to my CDs, [or] what may be on my iPod or on youtube (depending on [the] performance I like best). I feel the best [with] simply something spontaneous. While I enjoy learning different repertoires, genres and traditions, coming from a personal opinion, I don't really play too much in mainstream pop or anything trending because most people are performing that right now. I like to explore things that are off the beaten track, be it in music or in daily life. In my childhood, I enjoyed classical music, particularly Schubert's 'the trout,' Chopin, Bach, Vivaldi. As of late in listening to music, I have been exploring a lot in Asian music, particularly the classical music from India (both North Indian or Hindustani [and] South Indian) to Far and South East Asia."

"I do play classical guitar, acoustic and electric," Graeme adds, "and recently electric bass[,] which I built with the help of a close friend of mine who is an engineer. You may know my teacher Randy Raine-Reusch, as he and I have a strong friendship in music, [through] which we share similar tastes in music and in particular musical instruments. I also study with a music teacher from Peru, Rene Hugo Sanchez."

The email concludes with quick answers to three of the questions on Michael's original list that Graeme has not yet covered. "Your date is correct. I am thirty-six, born in 1977," he writes. As for recording, "I do record music mainly for documentation, and sometimes I may give my music to those who are interested, friends and family." Finally, regarding his diagnosis, "I was diagnosed quite early in childhood around the age you mentioned, but my mother is best to answer the last question. I hope this helps. Sincerely, Graeme."

There remain a few more unanswered questions as well, and Deborah is kind enough to fill in the blanks on those.

"Deborah here," she announces in a post-script to Graeme's email. Graeme, or Gray, as she usually calls him, explains Deborah, was diagnosed in 1980 at two-and-a-half years of age: "Because Gray was affectionate with us, his parents, the diagnostic team decided he didn't fit classic autism and diagnosed him with 'aphasia' with autistic features, because he didn't understand or speak any language. When he was six, he had language, though he was still delayed and his diagnosis changed to 'PDD-NOS— pervasive developmental delay [disorder] not otherwise specified.' By the time he was nine, the definition of autism had broadened enough that ever since, he has been diagnosed with classic autism. He's also been described as having high-functioning autism [i.e. low support-needs autism], but not Asperger's because he does have some cognitive deficits in executive functioning, particularly numbers and scheduling."[2]

Graeme started playing music when he was just one year old. "A toy piano was his favorite Christmas present that year," Deborah recalls. "Graeme was always strongly drawn to sounds, especially musical sounds, and would choose an object that produced a sound or tone over any conventional toy. When he was about six years old, we tried him in a music group for children, but he wouldn't leave the drum and was asked to leave the class. At that point, we were very fortunate to meet Dr. Johanne Brodeur, a music therapist who recognized Graeme's gift of absolute pitch and his ability to discriminate ten different notes played simultaneously on the piano. She taught him to read and even write music before he could read or write English, when his language was still fairly limited for his age, and worked with him weekly on many Western instruments until he was thirteen. He had an electric keyboard that he played constantly. Then he was put on a medication for his anxiety and disruptive behavior that reduced his creativity and his fine motor skills for a few years, during which time he listened to music but didn't play it."

In his later teens, Graeme began to develop an interest in instruments from different parts of the world. "For his seventeenth birthday, he astonished us by asking for a balalaika," Deborah remembers. "I still have no idea where that desire originated."

For Michael the ethnomusicologist, Graeme's interest in the balalaika comes as no surprise at all: after all, Michael thinks to himself while reading

2. The designation Asperger's syndrome (Asperger disorder), though still widely used, is no longer recognized as an official diagnostic category, per the most recent, fifth edition of the *Diagnostic and Statistical Manual of Mental Disorders: DSM-5* (American Psychiatric Association 2013a). People formerly diagnosed with Asperger's syndrome are now diagnosed under the broader umbrella term Austism Spectrum Disorder (ASD), assuming they meet the diagnostic criteria of an autism spectrum condition. If they do not, they may alternatively be diagnosed with Social (Pragmatic) Communication Disorder (SCD), which represents a new addition to the list of diagnosable conditions included in DSM-5 (American Psychiatric Association 2013b).

Deborah's remarks, what musically curious seventeen-year-old would not be intrigued by a giant, guitar-like instrument from Russia in the shape of a triangle?

"When we found one for him," Deborah adds regarding the balalaika and Graeme, "he researched teachers in the area and began lessons with [the Vancouver-based balalaika player] Bibs Ekkel."

"When Gray was in his late teens," Deborah continues, "our friend[,] the musicologist [and visionary computer scientist] Jaron Lanier, came to visit and through him, Gray met Randy Raine-Reusch, and began lessons with him, which have continued for around twenty years. Graeme will tell you about his work with Randy and his other teacher Rene Hugo-Sanchez."

Finally, Deborah tackles a question on Michael's list about the types of therapy Graeme has received for his autism, specifically those outside of music therapy: "Graeme was born before there were any therapies available for children with autism. He attended a wonderful preschool for special needs children, which exposed him to musical instruments and sign language, and increased his language. Because I studied and taught at the Linguistics Department at [the University of British Columbia], we had connections to researchers and practitioners in speech and audiology who were able to provide him with early language and social therapy. He was the first child with autism to be integrated into the regular school system in Vancouver and had a full-time aide."

In Michael's next email exchange with Graeme, he narrows the scope of questions to one of Graeme's principal areas of musical interest: the classical music traditions of India.

"What is it about North Indian and South Indian music that you like and that you find so interesting?" Michael types to Graeme.

"In regards to my fascinations with musics from South Asia, particularly in North and South Indian classical music, I found their use [of] raagas quite fascinating," Graeme replies, using an archaic spelling, raagas, over the more common *ragas*. "Aside from simply calling a raaga a scale, which is true, there [are] more components to it. In the North Indian or Hindustani system, in each raaga there is a thaat [thāt] (assigned mode, or some raags [raagas] may not have an assigned mode). Raags use a wide range of scales from pentatonic [five note], six-note scales or seven-note scales, and so on. Some of the thaats do correspond to what we know as modes, but the notation in music from India, be it north or south, is based on a non-fixed solfeggio, so in other words, while we use fixed notes, harmonic structures in chords, scales and melodies[,] over there it's more about the use of singular notes, and based on an aural tradition; training is taught from teacher to student through singing and vocalization. The use of rhythm there is cyclical, and it's a whole other ball game. The use of microtones does differ [between the North and the South] ... [I]n both systems the rules are similar [though] they do differ in some ways. In turn, [Indian] microtones differ from quarter tones found in Turkish, Arabic, and Persian music."

Michael is impressed by Graeme's knowledge on these topics. His descriptions of the raga and thāt systems are as good as or better than many Michael has seen in music textbooks and graduate student research papers, and Graeme is just warming up.

"Many other cultures, including in Myanmar (Burma) and in Vietnam, also use a similar system," Graeme continues, moving further into the challenging terrain of cross-cultural musical comparison. "In Myanmar, their classical system, while developed a bit differently than [in] neighbouring India[,] they share some things in common. Similar use of modes is found in Vietnam as well. Randy and I use whatever musical instrument comes to mind, be it a stringed instrument or percussion, depending on what lesson we feel like covering. In the end, a large part in music is to have fun. I'm also very passionate towards the musics of South America. As for my saz [a long-necked, lute-type string instrument from Turkey], I do have others from this region [i.e., other stringed instruments of related types], including a Greek bouzouki, Cretian Laouto, and a Joura (a medium length of bouzouki). There is something of a family [of these instruments in my collection]."

Conversation 1: July 4, 2014

In planning for their next dialogue, Michael convinces Graeme (with some help from Deborah) to meet online for a live chat session using the platform Google Hangouts. He explains that this will allow for more spontaneity than the back-and-forth emailing format they have been using up to this point. Graeme is initially hesitant but agrees to give it a try.

Graeme is new to Hangouts, and he and Michael experience some difficulties getting connected. On top of that, Graeme is a late riser, and it's still pretty early in the morning out on the west coast in Vancouver. As if all that were not enough, Graeme has not had his morning coffee yet, and by his own admission he does *not* do well without coffee. He gets agitated and a bit out of sorts, but following a brief troubleshooting phone conversation with him, Deborah, and Michael all on the line—and after that, a couple more false starts—the connection is finally achieved and Graeme starts to feel better.

"Hello Michael. I see your contact in my google chat," Graeme types in this, his first-ever Hangouts post.

"Hello Gray," Michael posts in reply. "Nice talking with you for a minute there on the phone, and I'm glad you got your coffee. ☺ "

"Yes, apologies for being grumpy this morning."

"No problem at all," Michael affirms.

"I'm also getting my coffee in now so we may proceed with this chat. ☺ "

Michael starts by asking Graeme what excites him about music the most: The sounds? The structures? The instruments? He is hoping to orient the conversation towards topics Graeme will be most eager to discuss, and also to keep the focus clear.

"I love the theory component in music altogether," Graeme writes back, "no matter the tradition behind it. And also the exploration [of] seeing who and what is out there. That is what drew me to 'world music' to begin with."

Michael notes that Graeme has placed the phrase "world music" in scare quotes. Ethnomusicologists frequently do this to emphasize the thorny nature of the construct of "world music" itself, but that rarely happens outside of the scholarly realm, which makes him curious about Graeme's usage. However, Michael decides to delay asking him about it until after they have followed through on the music theory topic.

"So it seems that the systems behind the music are what interest you the most, right?" Michael types.

"Yes, that is a huge part of it," Graeme replies, "but also just listening to the music gives me a calming sensation that nothing else at the moment can do so."

As the conversation unfolds, Graeme shares with Michael his interests in areas extending well beyond music per se: hiking, wildlife photography, and DIY (do it yourself) projects involving the building of electric circuits and musical instruments.

"I built an electric [guitar] and bass guitar thanks in huge part to my friend's wood workshop. I did the wiring for both projects," Graeme tells Michael proudly, following up by emailing him a photograph of the bass guitar.

"Wow!" Michael exclaims. "That must have been a big project. You must be a very talented builder *and* electrician!"

"The electronics is self-taught pretty much, and both were huge projects. If you saw them from a distance you might think that Gibson or Fender [the two major manufacturers of electric bass guitars] made them. But there are unique features in the wood work and pick guard, for example, [which] these two companies often do not do with their products. I looked on the Internet and saw some similar examples but none quite like my projects. They blend the best of both worlds for features in their wiring, volume and tone controls."

"Fantastic! Do you play those instruments very often?"

"My two guitars I play most often, and secondly I have been focusing a lot on my Greek bouzouki and Laouto from Crete, particularly with Dromoi (which means roads), the Greek equivalent to Maqam [Arabic modes] found in old Rebetika music, particularly from [the] 1900s to 1930s. Depends on mood. I love having the freedom and flexibility of choosing what instrument I feel like playing. Sometimes it is at the spur of the music."

"The spur of the *music* or the spur of the *moment*?" Michael asks.

"Right now not much of the spur of the moment," Graeme quips. "When waking up I do like the quiet now and then. ☺ "

Michael appreciates the joke, though he is still hoping for clarification of Graeme's spur of the music remark.

"So you did mean to write 'the spur of the music' then? OK. Please tell me what you mean by that. It's an interesting phrase!"

"Oh, I meant spur of the moment."

"Ah, OK. ☺ "

"Again, just the lack of thought process when waking up. I'm in zombie state right now."

"I understand, and we all make those kinds of mistakes. Still, though— spur of the music; I kind of like that idea. It's like the music kicks you in the side and gets your attention. ☺ "

"Yes," Graeme agrees. "That is what happens in composition often."

The conversation has suddenly taken an interesting and unexpected turn!

"Yes, that's true!!" Michael exclaims. "Tell me about how you compose."

" ...To answer your question, I first learned standard five bar [i.e., five-line staff] notation when studying in music therapy. This was way before meeting up with Randy [Raine-Reusch]. But for a long time I forgot much of the basics in this composition. It's coming back to me now because I use tablature a lot, especially for guitar or similar stringed instruments."

"Do you draw upon the different theoretical systems you have studied –
raga, maqam, dromoi – in your own compositions?"

"Oh yes, I have books on these subjects too. Which I enjoy consulting
now and then."

"What are the titles of a couple of those books? I'm an ethnomusicologist,
so I'm always interested in good sources of information."

"Ah, one of the titles for the books I have for the raaga is a reprint of
the 'The Raagas of North Indian music' [*The Ragas of Northern Indian Music*]
by Alain Danielou (1968). When it comes to theory, I have always loved 'the
heavier in knowledge the better.' ☺ "

"Ah, yes, Danielou," Michael echoes. "That is a very important book.
I'm glad you have consulted it."

"It's a great read too," Graeme adds.

"Yes, it certainly is!" Michael agrees, experiencing a rush of music-
theory-geek camaraderie with Graeme.

Judging by Graeme's enthusiasm for high-grade studies of Indian music
theory, Michael speculates that his sphere of interest probably extends to
math as well.

"Are you also interested in mathematics?" Michael asks Graeme.
"Music theory and math have so much in common. Those interests often
go together for people."

"Yes, I am; both music and math are tied together," Graeme affirms.
"But I'm also an audio-orientated learner. For some reason my math is
nowhere as good as my music. I leave the math to a friend of mine who is
an engineer. He can do calculus on paper without the aid of a calculator. So
I trust him with the math. ☺ "

"That sounds like a good mix of talents. Is your friend also autistic?"
Michael inquires.

"No, but he is very bright in his own way."

A great line, Michael thinks to himself, smiling.

"Do you have friends that are autistic?" Michael asks Graeme next.

"Yes, but we [have] different taste[s] and things in life that interest us. I have a couple friends with autism, but my social circle is often with those who don't have autism. It is just how it came to be. My friend Daniel Ouellet, who does the math, is a mechanical engineer."

"I see. Now in one of your earlier emails, you mentioned Randy and one other teacher, who I think was from Peru. Please remind me of his name."

"Yes, that is my teacher Rene Hugo Sanchez. ... He is a very good teacher and friend, one I draw a lot of knowledge from. ... We are in the process of collecting songs right now from all the regions in Peru. It's a small country compared to others like Brazil in South America, but that part of the world is a treasure chest for music. In Peru the departments (similar to a state or province) are so small, but each one has several different regional styles of music. This is what drew me to studying and appreciating Peruvian music. ... I love studying the alternate tuning systems for guitar, charango or mandolin. They are very inventive. Some involve using capos partially set to bass strings only."

"You are quite knowledgeable, Graeme. I can see that you practice what you preach re: 'the heavier in knowledge the better.' You must be an excellent student, and scholar!"

"It's an addiction of mine I must confess. ☺ "

"Hey, there are worse addictions, to be sure! ☺ "

"That is true."

"It's an addiction of mine, too," Michael admits, "but it's also my job, so that's worked out pretty well. ☺ "

"... Anyhow," Graeme writes, "I do have to have my lunch if you don't mind. ... My stomach is talking to me right now and I came to believe it has its own will when it wants its food. ☺ "

Michael chuckles along with Graeme's smiley-face emoji. "OK, I look forward to continuing this another time, perhaps next week," he proposes. "I'll talk to your mom about trying to set up a time that works for everyone. Bye for now, and thanks!"

"You're welcome. Please keep in touch ...."

"Adios!"

"Adios."

Conversation 2: July 7, 2014

Based on the success of their first chat session, Graeme and Michael (with Deborah's assistance) schedule a follow-up for three days later.

"Hi Gray, I'm here now," Michael posts after logging on.

"Hi Michael. Good morning. I'm waking up still."

"Ah, here it's already 2:00 in the afternoon, so I've been up for a while. Good morning to you!"

"It's around 11:00 a.m. [here] so I'm not quite there in the afternoon yet," Graeme responds. "By the time my afternoon rolls around you will be in the evening. Fascinating things time zones are."

"Indeed!" Michael affirms. "I wanted to follow up on a couple of things you said last time, OK?"

"Sure, of course. And they are?"

"You talked about the 'calming sensation' that music had on you, and that that was something 'that nothing else at the moment can do.' Could you tell me more about what that feels like, how it helps you, and also what *kinds* of music have that effect?"

"Ah yes, the only way I can describe that to you is it's sort of narcotic. I mean to say [that] as soon as I pick up a musical instrument to play it, or as soon as I put my headphones on and select something I want to listen [to], something quite different comes over me. However, the effect when listening [to] or playing the music [only] lasts for a while[;] it does not last for a whole day. Experience and mood-wise it does change my outlook on the day; it makes it a lot better. There are times if I'm too stressed out, when I take a break from everything and just simply declutter the thoughts in my brain and take the time to organize them. There is not a specific time limit as to how long this experience lasts; each experience in playing or listening to music is different from one to the next."

"So do different types of music affect your emotions in different ways?" Michael inquires. "I know you have done research on the ragas and [the Arab] maqamat [modes]. In such systems, say, with ragas, they have associations with specific mood-states, seasons, times of day, etc. I'm wondering whether you have any kind of music/emotion system like that personally, whether related to existing systems of different musics or otherwise. Please enlighten me on this!"

"Yes, when I was young (childhood to youth) much of my exposure to music was European classical music. In particular my favorites went from Schubert, Chopin, Bach, Vivaldi and so on. At the time I did not know what this music was. I just knew I enjoyed listening to it. To this day I cannot stand music that is too loud, or something too commercial (stuff in the Top 40 or what's played on the radio these days). But I do enjoy a wide range from traditional to some contemporary, which includes some experimental (free improvisation, avant-garde, and so on). I have noted that each raag may be connected with an emotion or several emotions, but I like to think that is the behavior of music in general. Depends on the mood of the listener: the music here is a lens that amplifies the person's state of mind."

"So when you seek that calming effect as a listener, you still mainly go to the classics? Schubert, Chopin, Bach, etc.?"

"It may depend on the mood I'm in, but usually I seek happiness, joy, relaxation, calming. From another experience, I found in music [that] I enjoy following and learning to play by ear when listening to some pieces. I have a lot of old African guitar music, particularly from the 1940s through the 1970s, found on CD and LP (Record). I enjoy the challenge of music, which it presents in both playing and theory as well."

"Excellent. Thank you! On to other questions then!"

"And what are your other questions then?" Graeme fires back. Michael takes the opportunity to ask the "world music" question he has been holding in reserve until now.

"I noted in our last chat that you put quotation marks around the phrase 'world music' when I had not. I thought that was very sophisticated of you and I have my guesses as to why you did it, but I'm interested in your own explanation. Why did you choose to do that?"

"Ah, I often do this as a means to emphasize what world music is," Graeme begins. "People often have it marked as another genre, but because world music involves numerous traditions [up] to contemporary musics, it's really not just a single genre of music. I prefer to think of it as a spectrum that includes numerous genres. Often when explaining this to most people, usually they are curious and they may not understand what world music is. It is a process of discovery for the person listening to it. Not just a genre. Sometimes boxing things into genres and labels may not work all the time. I found that to be the case with world music, when thinking about this particular aspect of it."

"Excellent answer, and it makes me wonder: do you have similar thoughts about autism and the autism spectrum?"

"Yes," Graeme affirms, "because in autism, I also found that everyone is different from their case, to my case and so on. I do agree with the term 'spectrum' but we still have lots to learn; there is a lot of misinformation out there still. I prefer for people to see me for who I am as a person and not judge me based upon what they hear from Hollywood or the media, which is often very inaccurate."

"I have another question, Graeme. This is one I've asked several of the other people I've spoken to for this project as well. Here it is: If you could wave a magic wand and your autism would be gone, would you do that or not?"

"For me, no. Some symptoms I would like to have gone, like stress triggers and so on, but I fear in the end my music may be lost too. Like you want to keep some old software on your computer you may not run in the newer systems but you need to reformat and upgrade as things develop and improve. I worry that if it was the case [that my autism was gone] my music would go [away] along with the symptoms."

"Anything else you would fear losing, other than your music?"

"I'm not so sure, but I'm certain I will find something. For the most part I'm very happy being the individual who I am. A part of life's journey is that it is an ongoing process in my own self-discovery."

"Thanks! So I'd like to continue a little while longer if you're OK with that, but please let me know how much more time you have here today."

"Ah. OK. I'm available until 12:00 p.m., because my stomach is impatient when it comes to needing its food. I have tried arguing with it and lost that argument a long time ago."

Graeme and Michael exchange emoji chuckles over this remark.

"OK, so just a couple of minutes," Michael confirms. "One more question then. Here it comes!"

"OK."

"The [publications] in which our correspondence is going to be included will hopefully be read by quite a few people: autistic people, non-autistic people, musicians, non-musicians, scholars, non-scholars. We have an opportunity here to change the way people think about autism and autistic people, both with respect to music and otherwise. With that in mind, what would you most like to express to the world at large, as it were, from your perspective as an autistic musician, a thoughtful person, and a caring individual?"

Michael waits a couple of minutes as Graeme composes his reply.

Finally, it appears.

"I would like to express to the rest of the world," proclaims Graeme, "that you judge me for who I am as a person not based on what I am. Autism is a part of who I am but I do not allow for it to define me. In conclusion, as you meet us you will find we are just as diverse and different from one to the next [as other people are]. We all have our own life stories. All we ask for is simply to be treated with the same respect as we would be [if we were not autistic] when it comes to interacting with society in general."

"Thank you, Gray. That is beautifully said. I've very much enjoyed these two chats. Do you have any final thoughts to share or questions for me before we sign off?"

"I'm pleased to contribute to this [project] in the end. Mom has written her Ph.D., [in] which I'm pretty much her subject. So I'm somewhat familiar with academia when it comes to sharing my experiences in autism. ... Specifically the Ph.D. [dissertation] was about my language comprehension or lack thereof when I was very young. If you met me at the age of two, I was delayed and I had my own means of communicating with the outside world. So Mom had the time and dedication to write a diary of this and now this diary is her Ph.D. [Gibson, D. 2011] ... And there is one more thing. I'm happy to share [with] you my photos when it comes to my bird and wildlife photography. One of my rare experiences was I had a redwing blackbird land on my hand. I had no food, no seed. I was standing in the park, and he checked my camera out first then decided to land on my hand. I got my iPhone out and snapped a photo. I was left stunned in my experience but amazed I was able to keep a photo record of this."

"Oh, yes, great. I'd love to see that—please send it along! Have a great day!"

"You too. Sunny here today, so I'm hoping for some good photos. Cheers. Adios."

"Ditto. Adios!"

Red-Winged Blackbird

Graeme sends Michael not just one red-winged blackbird photo but a couple of them, as well as a recording of him performing a modal improvisation on his Greek bouzouki.

"The scale," Graeme says of the recording, "is something like a minore dromoi (which is Greek for scale[;] the correct translation is road); the closest analogy we know is the natural minor scale as found in numerous genres of music. In traditional Greek music[,] particularly the early rebetika from the early 1910s to 1930s[,] they often used scales that bore the same names as their Turkish and Arabic equivalents although lacking much of the quartertones. Some current bouzouki makers may add custom frets to ... achieve the quartertones [for modes like] Hijaz, Hijazkiar, Kiurdi, Houseini, Nihavent, Sabah, Segah, Usak and so on. A scale with the same name[,] Segah[,] is also found in Persian music. Some are regional scales like Piraeus[,] which is one of the areas where Rebetika emerged; the other is Smyrna[,] which is Izmir in today's Turkey."

Graeme provides detailed information about his photographs as well. The one that appeals to Michael the most is of a female red-winged blackbird.

"Here is a favourite pic of mine I took this year in June to July at Jericho Beach, Vancouver, Canada," Graeme writes. "I used my Canon T3i with 18-55 mm starter lens for this photo and this female red wing black bird did not seem frightened or fazed by this experience. Female red wing black birds don't have the red shoulder pads as their male counterparts [do]. They do share the same type of call when communicating."

The female red-winged blackbird photograph is captivating. Against a backdrop of wildflowers and lush greenery, the little bird perches contentedly on Graeme's outstretched left hand. Her shoulder pads indeed show no red, and her coloring is more brown than black, except for her tail feathers and a distinctive pattern of black striping across her breast. With head cocked ever so slightly, she registers a bemused curiosity that is as sweet as can be. She looks so calm and trusting as she grips Graeme's fingers with her tiny feet. Her black tail feathers flank outward to the edges of his hand, her wings tucked behind her back as though in an avian yoga pose.

The more Michael looks at the picture, the more he is drawn in; and the more drawn in he becomes, the more deeply he is moved. Tears come to Michael's eyes, though he is not quite sure why. It is a precious moment, and one in which he feels that he has come to know Graeme more deeply than before.

Closing Thoughts

A useful definition of the term *theory* appears in the second edition of ethnomusicologist Bruno Nettl's book *The Study of Ethnomusicology: Thirty-One Issues and Concepts.* Theory, Nettl suggests in that 2005 publication, is essentially comprised of nothing more nor less than "intellectual positions from which interpretations emerge" (Nettl 2005, 452): short, to the point, and spot on.

It is to such a conception of theory – combined with Bakan's earlier-cited definition of ethnomusicology as the study of how people make and experience music, and of why it matters to them that they do (Bakan 2015, 117) – that we have turned in writing this chapter. In so doing, we have consciously pushed back against the conventions of representational approaches in ethnographic work in order to model and advocate for re-presentational alternatives. Whether positioned as ethnomusicologists or anthropologists, clinicians or ethnographers, medical scientists or scholars of medical humanities, it behooves contemporary researchers in these and related fields to foreground the words, sentiments, ideas, and modes of expression of the people about whom they write, and with whom they share discursive and other communicative space.

It is our hope that the discursive space created in this chapter, especially in its re-presentation of the formative dialogues that prefigured the work, offers a useful exemplar. These dialogues provide clear, empirical evidence that Graeme Gibson needs no one to speak for him; he speaks perfectly well for himself. That said, the mode of presentation/re-presentation modeled here demonstrates a realm of possibility in which an interlocutor/scholar like Michael Bakan can potentially serve a useful purpose. The conversational medium of re-presentation ensures that Graeme's words and ideas cannot be isolated from the original context of their emergence: deep, engaged, socially connected dialogue; it embodies the profusely social way through which we, the co-authors of this chapter, have come to know each other.

This reality in itself contests pervasive essentialisms that surround discourses on autism and the social capacities of people on the autism spectrum. Moreover, it offers readers a productive lens through which to perceive the modes of knowledge production through which this particular chapter – and indeed so much other scholarly work as well – has come to fruition: conversation and consternation, reciprocity and resistance, negotiation and contestation, collaboration and confusion. Re-presentational ethnography is at its core more process-oriented than product-driven, and in this respect it offers important inflection points for revisiting and rethinking the very project of representation as a pathway to critical thought and inquiry.

In re-presentational ethnography, the intellectual positions to be considered – the theories, to invoke Nettl once again – are inherent to the ethnographic encounter itself, and, more specifically, to conversational encounters preserved in dialogue transcripts. The interpretations that emerge from such transcripts are not provided *to* those who read our works but are rather arrived at *by* those readers as they are invited into the discourses that generated the transcripts in the first place.

Finally, these readers gain the agency to interpret the work on their own terms, to generate their own theoretical positions from which to move towards new understandings based on a key form of empirical evidence: re-presented dialogue. In the case of this chapter, we expect that a key takeaway for most readers will be that the individual at its center, Graeme Gibson, is uniquely qualified to speak to the issues at hand—because he is the one living them. The subjects of ethnographies are the world's leading experts at being who they are. As such, they deserve to be respected on their own terms, and to really be listened to – closely and carefully, thoroughly and thoughtfully – as well.

Re-presentational approaches offer key gateways to new ways of understanding built upon the integrity of such forms of respect and listening. Moreover, they are perhaps most acutely needed in the medical humanities, committed as these disciplines are to redressing the long and torturous histories of dehumanization and marginalization that have issued in the wake of pathology-rooted models for understanding human difference. As we negotiate the medical humanities, we must negotiate the terms of who speaks for whom and, in that process, privilege the voices of people across the full spectrum of human diversities as they speak for, about, and on behalf of themselves. We must recognize and accept that *all* persons everywhere are the world's leading experts at being who they are, and we must, in turn, aspire to honor their unique expertise.

There is so much we can learn about personhood, autism, music, neurodiversity, and the myriad intersections between these complex domains of human experience and expression from the individuals who embody these ontological realities. Now it is time to truly listen to what they have to say.

Works Cited

American Psychiatric Association. 2013a. *Diagnostic and Satistical Manual of Menatl Disorders: DSM-5.* 5th ed. Washington, D.C.: American Psychiatric Association.

American Psychiatric Association. 2013b. "Social (Pragmatic) Communication Disorder" [DSM-5 online fact sheet]. Washington, D.C.: American Psychiatric Association. Accessed October 14, 2022. https://www.psychiatry.org/File%20Library/Psychiatrists/Practice/DSM/APA_DSM-5-Social-Communication-Disorder.pdf.

Bakan, Michael B. 2015. "'Don't Go Changing to Try and Please Me': Combating Essentialism through Ethnography in the Ethnomusicology of Autism." *Ethnomusicology* 59, no. 1: 116–44.

Bakan, Michael B. 2016. "Music, Autism, and Disability Aesthetics." Colloquy: On the Disability Aesthetics of Music, convened by Blake Howe and Stephanie Jensen-Moulton. *Journal of the American Musicological Society* 69, no. 2: 548-53.

Bakan, Michael B. 2018. "Music and Autism, Representation and Re-presentation: An Ethnomusicological Perspective." In *Autism in Translation: An Intercultural Conversation on Autism Spectrum Conditions*, edited by Elizabeth Fein and Clarice Rios, 109-128. Cham, Switzerland: Palgrave Macmillan.

Bakan, Michael B., with Mara Chasar, Graeme Gibson, Elizabeth J. Grace, Zena Hamelson, Dotan Nitzberg, Gordon Peterson, Maureen Pytlik, Donald Rindale, Amy Sequenzia, and Addison Silar. 2018. *Speaking for Ourselves: Conversations on Life, Music, and Autism.* New York: Oxford University Press.

Bakan, Michael B., with Mara Chasar, Graeme Gibson, Elizabeth J. Grace, Zena Hamelson, Dotan Nitzberg, Gordon Peterson, Maureen Pytlik, Donald Rindale, Amy Sequenzia, and Addison Silar. 2021.

Music and Autism: Speaking for Ourselves. New York: Oxford University Press.

Danielou, Alain. 1968. *The Ragas of Northern Indian Music*. London: Barrie and Rockliff.

Fein, Elizabeth, and Clarice Rios, ed. 2018. *Autism in Translation: An Intercultural Conversation on Autism Spectrum Conditions*. Cham, Switzerland: Palgrave Macmillan.

Gibson, Deborah. 2011. "The Early Lexical Acquisition of a Child with Autism Spectrum Disorder." Doctoral Dissertation (Language and Literacy Education), University of British Columbia.

Gibson, Graeme. "Museum of World Music." Accessed March 15, 2022. museumofworldmusic.com.

Gibson, William. 1984. *Neuromancer*. New York: Ace Books.

Nettl, Bruno. 2005. *The Study of Ethnomusicology: Thirty-One Issues and Concepts*. New Edition (2nd). Urbana: University of Illinois Press.

Nitzberg, Dotan, and Michael B. Bakan. 2019. "Resilience and Adaptive Management in Piano Pedagogy for Individuals on the Autism Spectrum." In *Cultural Sustainabilities: Music, Media, Language, Advocacy*, edited by Timothy J. Cooley, 249-61. Urbana and Chicago: University of Illinois Press.

Sterponi, Laura. 2015. "A Commentary on 'Music and Autism, Representation and Re-presentation: An Ethnomusicological Perspective' by Michael B. Bakan." Discussant remarks presented at Autism Spectrum Disorders in Global, Local and Personal Perspective: A Cross-Cultural Workshop, Rio De Janeiro, Brazil, September 2015.

2

Lost for Words: Aphasia and the Neuroscience of Self-Identity

Brian Dolan, *University of California, San Francisco*

Abstract:

Since at least the seventeenth century, philosophers have contemplated the role of language in creating self-identity. It has been posited that memories of life experiences are configured through narrative, without which states of consciousness would exist as disconnected fragments in the mind. For modern narrative theorists, such autobiographical stories constitute how people understand themselves and make meaning in life. For medical humanists, the field of narrative medicine has encouraged dialogue between patients and providers about states of health. However, a range of neurological disorders can impact language processing, and therefore can affect narrative constructions of self and the articulation of quality of life. This article looks at the history of aphasia – the loss of language often associated with stroke – and how this illness has informed philosophical conceptions of self and challenged clinical rehabilitation efforts that aim to "reconnect" patients to the world through their use of language.

I talk to myself. I even talk to myself in the third person. Sometimes when I hit a bad golf shot, I yell, "Goddammit, Brian." But over many years of playing miserable golf, I have learned that the inner monologue I have, where I offer commentary on my performance, helps me to calm down. I came to consider it therapeutic, and indeed I may have been right.

According to a group of psychologists at Michigan State University and the University of Michigan, if you saw an fMRI while I am admonishing myself in this manner, it would look something like this. (Figure 1) It seems that my tendency to talk to myself – which is something most people do – is scientifically called "self-talk," and it is a subject of interest to neuroscientists. In an article published in *Nature*, the Michigan team argued that this process demonstrates "how a linguistic shift that promotes psychological distance from the self modulates emotional responses," leading to self-control (Moser et al. 2017). Whereas at one time, muttering to yourself might have signaled senility or insanity, it is now seen as having therapeutic and mental health benefits. Indeed, learning enhancement resources provided by Eastern Washington University encourage students to practice this, saying

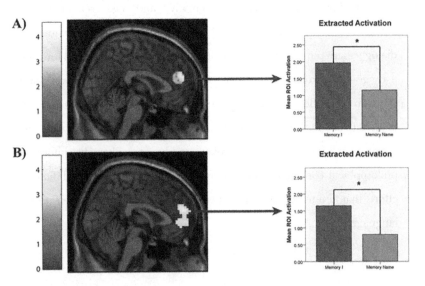

Figure 1: fMRI brain imaging results from showing a region of the medial prefrontal cortex identified as playing a role in self-referential processing (subject referring to "I" as opposed to one's own name). Reproduced under creative commons license from Moser, J.S., Dougherty, A., Mattson, W.I. et al. Third-person self-talk facilitates emotion regulation without engaging cognitive control: Converging evidence from ERP and fMRI. *Sci Rep* 7, 4519 (2017).

that: "Self-talk influences your academic performance and your well-being. Controlling your thoughts is the gateway to controlling your emotions and behaviors" (Eastern Washington University 2022). A group of psychologists from UC Berkeley studied how self-talk allows self-distancing, called a "fly-on-the-wall" perspective of oneself, that allows people to reflect on painful experiences without ruminating, underscoring the relevance of this process in cognitive therapy (Kross et al. 2014, 304-324). If you objectify yourself – pause and ask, "What are you doing, Brian?" – it can help to isolate a traumatic event so it can be chiseled out in one's psyche and managed more effectively.

Talking, however, does more than aid self-control or generate billable hours for a psychoanalyst. Philosophers and social scientists have long speculated that narrative, say autobiographical stories, create the self. I will elaborate on this shortly, but to help paint a portrait of the problem that I address here, I refer briefly to how the self and language have been historically connected. The seventeenth-century philosopher John Locke famously wrote, in his *Essay Concerning Human Understanding*, that self-identity (and this is often synonymous with "sense of self") is created when a conscious being reflects on their own history through memories. The "self" is defined as the continuity of consciousness, a self-awareness that is mediated by memory. It is a thought process that is somehow materially configured in the mind. As a post-scientific revolution philosopher, Locke's theory was distinctively different than attributing self to the equivalency of an immaterial soul implanted by God. Elaborating this Enlightenment understanding of self, narrative theorists posit that identity is primarily constituted in stories that recount past autobiographical events. Who we understand ourselves to be is not merely a recollection of random memories, but a logical ordering and interpretation of them that creates a life history. This story does not need to be spoken aloud; it can be formed from an internal monologue; self-talk can construct identity.

One can quickly see the problem that illness might pose to this configuration of self. A range of neurological disruptions can affect consciousness. Disorders can affect the ability to recall memories, or they can affect the ability to construct stories. Some patients lose the ability to dream, and for others, the inner monologue is permanently silenced. This essay explores how illness interferes with narratives of self in ways that might turn oneself into a disease. Because of the privilege we place upon language as a tool to define ourselves, we run the risk of mishandling that tool. But a deeper problem is this: what happens when language, a tool to define oneself, is taken away?

To some, the existential crisis that illness may generate – progressive dementia in elderhood, memory loss with Alzheimer's, the loss of language following stroke – may be outside the reach of clinical medicine. Questions about self or identity may seem more relevant to metaphysics or religion. But in fact, as many people whose views I will discuss have shown, there is direct clinical significance to thinking critically about language and how patients engage in dialogue with health care teams about states of health. Stories not only shape perceptions of self, but also perceptions of illness. This is crucial to assessing quality of life, which is recognized as an important outcome measure in post-stroke recovery efforts, but one which notoriously fails to let patients define what quality of life means. And the conceptual paradigms behind rehabilitation efforts continue to question how language shapes the inner self as well as how it connects us to the world.

While this essay, in part, questions the limits of language and the uses of narrative in illness identity formation, I acknowledge the irony that I, too, am telling a story, and that my interpretation of these issues is constructed largely with words offered by patients, clinicians, and academics. Therefore, in foreshadowing my conclusion, I offer no immediate alternative to accessing and representing inner states of being; I am, in that respect, lost for words. But I do hope that by re-reading the role of language, or its absence, in how we think about health and illness, we can increase our sensitivity to the very tools we take for granted.

Dr. Taylor was then a thirty-seven-year-old neuroanatomist who was building her career studying brain function, an interest motivated by her brother's schizophrenia, but then suddenly, something happened. She would later write, "I was literally thrown off balance when my right arm dropped completely paralyzed against my side. In that moment, I knew. *Oh my gosh, I was having a stroke! I'm having a stroke!* And in the next instant, the thought flashed through my mind, *Wow, this is so cool!*" (Taylor 2008, 44).

This is Jill Taylor reflecting on her chance to study a disorder from the patient's point of view, her own point of view, in what she called a remarkable "stroke of insight," which is also the title of her book describing her event. She suffered a hemorrhagic stroke right between Broca's and Wernicke's areas. (Figures 2 and 3) Broca's area has long been associated with language production, whereas Wernicke's area is associated with comprehension.

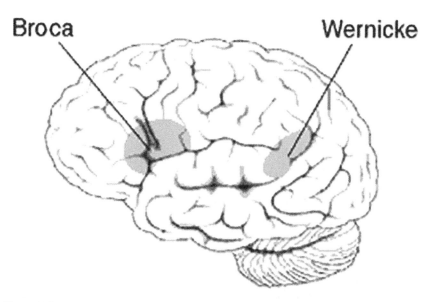

Figure 2: Diagram depicting Broca's area (front left of brain) and Wernicke's area (back left) from Wiki commons.

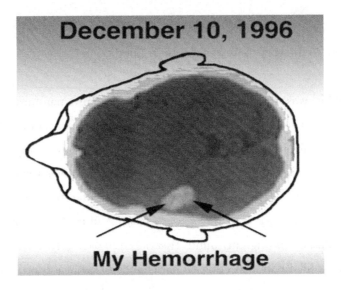

Figure 3: Scan of Dr. Jill Taylor's brain showing location of her hemorrhage, from TED talk (https://www.ted.com/speakers/jill_bolte_taylor).

Her stroke affected both functions, and for five weeks, she fell into what she provocatively called "a pervasive and enticing inner peace."

Dr. Taylor's self-reflection is unlike others who suffer a stroke. It's not unusual, given the position of the hemorrhage, to have affected language or to lose the ability to track time, thus breaking her life into "consecutive brief instances." What was unusual was how her stroke resulted in a new perception of her place in the universe:

> I morphed from feeling small and isolated to feeling enormous and expansive. I stopped thinking in language and shifted to taking new pictures of what was going on in the present moment. I was not capable of deliberating about past or future-related ideas because those cells were incapacitated. All I could perceive was right here, right now, and it was beautiful. My entire self-concept shifted as I no longer perceived boundaries that separated me from the entities around me (Taylor 2008, 68-69).

A number of comments that she made would suggest that she had lost herself, at least in the framework of Lockean philosophy. She stopped thinking in language; she couldn't track time; there was no sense of past or future, only the present moment. Yet she does not say she "lost" herself; she says her self-concept "shifted." This perspective seems to challenge the role of memory and language in making meaning of one's life. She somehow found beauty in being part of a non-linear universe.

Dr. Taylor describes an eight-year journey to return to a clinically-defined, fully functional status. But *en route* to this point, where she is able to give TED talks about her experience, she wondered who she would be when (and if) she arrived at that point of recovery. And, again, what is most unusual is her concern that she would *lose* what she had *gained* from the stroke: "Would it be possible for me to recover my perception of my *self*, where I exist as a single, solid, separate from the whole, without recovering the cells associated with my egotism. … Most importantly, could I retain my newfound sense of connection with the universe in the presence of my left hemisphere's individuality (Taylor 2008, 131-132)?"

There is something perversely disquieting in the idea that this patient lost nothing more than some brain cells; that, in her view, the bleeding in her head gave life to a hemispheric "individuality." Stroke stories are typically not about liberation. This is admittedly quite different from our conventional understanding of how people react in these situations.

Social scientists have for decades examined a broad range of conditions that inform a person's self-identity. The body itself is a central material and symbolic resource for self-construction, and scholars in disability studies, chronic illness, and aging have looked at how changes to the body cause a reconceptualization of oneself. This is a variable process corresponding to how one perceives the significance of their illness. Arthritic pain that advances with age becomes part of a self-identity as a state of normality because of widespread expectations that aging causes a deterioration of the body. Invoking one's age becomes an adaptive strategy for dealing with the disruptive effects of an illness (Hinojosa et al. 2008, 208).

In what ways do stroke patients typically feel that their self-identity has changed as a result of their experience? In the 1980s and 1990s, colleagues of mine from the University of California, San Francisco, Gaye Becker, and Sharon Kaufman, were researching how patients confront the disruption to life following stroke. They found that stroke may cause a person to rethink their own past to provide meaning for their current framework of illness. As Kaufman wrote in 1988, "the individual needs to 'repair' and 'heal' the self by revising and re-creating the biography so that it makes sense in light of the current changed circumstances of the individual's existence (Kaufman 1988, 217)." Reflecting on interviews with sixty-four patients, Kaufman found that their experience was characterized by a feeling of discontinuity between the pre-stroke self and the post-stroke "redefined self." Kaufman wrote: "When we asked patients, 'Do you feel you have recovered from the stroke?' or 'Do you feel your life is back to normal?' the answer was invariably 'no.' Even patients without a visible disability gave this answer, for they believe that they are physically, emotionally, or cognitively different from their pre-stroke selves" (Kaufman 1988, 219). The challenge of recovering from a severe illness "is integrating the same core self with new conditions – physical, social, and moral – for its expression" (Kaufman 1988, 225).

The questions being asked are fundamentally this: if your autobiography is a book, how do you rationalize a radical change of plot? How can my former healthy self be integrated with my current disrupted self and with whatever I will become? How can continuity be reestablished in the narrative of my life? The psychologist Rik Cheston at the University of Bristol seeks to understand dementia as an existential threat to people. He believes in the power of stories to help heal. "The creation of a story," he writes, "permits a world in which present dilemmas, uncertainties, and hopes can be lived through" (Cheston 1996, 583). Self-narratives create an opportunity for patients to recreate ideas in ways that help to explain the present. They are not just reexamining their life; they are rewriting it. To quote Cheston again, "It is through the self-narrative, the story that we tell ourselves, that the 'I', the author, creates a story in which the 'me' is the protagonist and is able to act out roles. The self as the author is able both to imagine the future and to reconstruct the past" (Cheston 1996, 582).

Medical sociologist Kathy Charmaz studied the effects of chronic illness on patients' self-image. She found that the longer a person suffers their illness, the more their previously positive self-images evaporate. Their memories of health became weaker. She writes: "Clearly, these chronically ill persons evince a heightened self-concern about the person they see themselves becoming and about valued self-images from the past which they have lost, sometimes irretrievably" (Charmaz 1983, 190). Suffering such losses, Charmaz says, "results in a diminished self" (Charmaz 1983, 169).

Scholars who study degenerative diseases or neurological disorders pay close attention to the reaction against memory loss, as well as to language deficits. The underlying assumption is that without these, there is no unity to life. As the philosopher Shaun Gallagher wrote in a 2000 article in *Trends in Cognitive Sciences*, "If I were unable to form memories of my life history, or were unable to access such memories, then I have nothing to interpret, nothing to narrate sufficient for the formation of self-identity. ... We use words to tell stories, and in these stories, we create what we call ourselves" (Gallagher 2000, 209).

Twenty years after the 1988 article by Kaufman that I cited earlier, a group of researchers led by the sociologist Ramon Hinojosa at the University of Florida conducted interviews over a two-year period with 122 stroke patients from Veterans Affairs who had varied functional capabilities. They sought to determine whether the patients had self-identity continuity, in their words, "a persistent sense that despite the stroke, one remains essentially unchanged" in their self-perception, their understanding of the meaning of life, or view of the future (Hinojosa et al. 2008, 211). The researchers stated that their expectation was that, like Becker and Kaufman found, "stroke would be discussed as being immensely disruptive." Surprisingly, one-third of their respondents offered narratives of continuity, using phrases such as "I'm the same" or "nothing much has changed" (Hinojosa et al. 2008, 212). They sometimes showed despair over their physical condition, but despair is not discontinuity. Even those with physical impairment constructed continuity, in part by referencing their connection to, and support from, their families.

It is true that inviting a comment about self-perception or identity is not an objective science, and these authors noted that the responses might have been culturally conditioned to meet normative expectations about well-being. They may have even been expressions evoking a desired state of being, similar to deploying the power of positive self-talk ("I'll be fine."). But the claim the authors are making is that a significant portion of their study held "a different self-understanding than those who characterized their post-stroke experiences with words like 'worthless,' 'meaningless,' 'useless,' and 'helpless'" (Hinojosa et al. 2008, 212). What did that one-third who maintained continuity draw upon that enabled them to have a different self-understanding? Were there cultural resources available in the 2000s that were not available twenty years earlier to help patients perceive continuity of self? Or to construct a story of one? Consider the rise of patient support and advocacy groups, and the proliferation of narrative exposition of illness. Many resources have been created to help people—patients as well as their families—keep hold of themselves in moments of disruption. Many of these point to the power of stories in our lives.

Today there is no shortage of autobiographical literature on the experience of illness. The concern of patient advocates to battle stigma, the assembly of support groups, a relative ease of publication, online fora, and social networks, all have created a community of those who want to hear from one another. However, much of the discussion provides a description of the disease or the experience living with it, rather than representing disease as an expression of a new self. There is a recent exception to this discussed (again) by Sharon Kaufman, who wrote about how her mother, who was a poet, described losing her "self" to dementia (Kaufman 2017, 549-568). While losing memories, the poet worked to make meaning of herself without being able to identify with a specific place and time. Not unlike stroke patients, her life was fragmented. But for a poet, fragmentation is a feature of creative life. That the poet was able to use the tools of her trade to shape her new identity is testimony to the power of language; she controlled the narrative.

It is important to control the narrative because the words of others may cast the wrong impression. The disease on which I am now going to focus is as old as Hippocrates, yet, throughout medical history, there was no reliable vocabulary to talk about what was happening to a person who lost the ability to speak. There were names – alalia, aphasia, aphemia, all referring vaguely to the same condition: consciousness without presence – but no diagnostic discourse existed (Henderson 1990, 85-88). In the absence of knowing what caused it, or what caused stroke itself, and with no cure to talk about, it remained a curiosity to be observed.

When we say "aphasia," today we are talking about a disorder of linguistic processing. Many diagnostic subcategories indicate deficits such as comprehension or anomia, the inability to find the right words. There is even an associated condition called "tip of the tongue" syndrome. It is estimated that a third of all stroke patients end up with some degree of aphasia, but as we saw, recovery is possible for some.

In the early nineteenth century, the French physician Jacques Lordat wrote one of the first comprehensive accounts of patients who were struck with aphasia. He published his account in 1843 though he was reporting on clinical observations over the previous decades. One of his cases described a visit to a priest who was thought to have suffered an apoplectic attack, a stroke. "When I arrived," Lordat wrote, "the supposed apoplectic was seated on his bed, wide awake; he received me courteously and openly. He seemed more concerned about me than about himself. I had come on horseback; the weather was bad. He made signs to indicate that I should first get warm and have a meal. This language, silent as it was, was sufficiently significant that everyone moved and obeyed" (Lordat 1843; trans. Riese and Hubert 1954, 237-242). (Figure 4)

This prelude to a physical exam may seem anecdotal, but in fact, it

Figure 4: Portrait of the French doctor Jacques Lordat (1773-1870), illustration by L Massard, from 1883. Courtesy of Wellcome Trust.

establishes a baseline that the physician will later use to assess the damage. Upon the introduction, the priest is civil, prioritizing his position as host over that of patient to the visiting doctor. He is offering hospitality in what is symbolically his own hospital, the residential quarters appended to the house of God. In fact, the priest is the epitome of a patient, embodying the meaning of the word as someone patiently enduring their suffering.

But then the priest broke down. When attempting to issue more instructions to his servants, he vocalized sounds that no one could comprehend. He became agitated. As Lordat observed, "He showed his impatience by two very vigorous words, one of which was I, and the other the most forceful swearword in our language, which begins with the letter F" (Jacyna 2009, 31). The fact that the patient was himself a servant of God whose last resort was shouting expletives was a salient point for Lordat: "As he was a man of spirit and a priest, I thought he was ignorant of the meaning of the terms that he pronounced." Becoming impatient, the priest's ailment had caused a discrepancy between his authentic self and the profane self that was expressed through disease. It was as if he was possessed. He had lost that inner self-control; and in nineteenth-century polite society, as the historian Roger Smith reminds us in his book *Inhibition*, using reason to suppress the inner beast was regarded as the hallmark of civilization. Did this disease return us to some primitive state (Smith 1992)?

Another question, asked by nearly every stroke patient throughout history is the following: what did I do to deserve this? We should remember that the term "stroke" itself comes from a common sentence describing someone who was "struck by the hand of God." An apoplectic fit was just the Greek term describing someone who suddenly falls to the ground as if struck by a thunderbolt. That a priest was the victim of God's punishing hand was somewhat of a moral, if not medical, mystery. The priest never fully recovered. However, in a curious change of events, he was later summoned to visit the house of the physician. This time, Lordat himself was now the victim of a strike from God's hand.

It was the summer of 1825 and Lordat was not feeling well. Upon receiving a guest, he tried to offer a welcome but remained silent. "My thoughts were ready," he later wrote, "but the sounds that should convey them to my informant were no longer at my disposal. Turning away in dismay, I said to myself: *So, it is true that I can no longer speak!*" (Riese and Hubert 1954, 237). It is interesting to note that he could still talk to himself. He continued his self-observation:

> My impediment increased rapidly: within twenty-four hours all but a few words eluded my grasp. ... I was no longer able to grasp the ideas of others, for the very amnesia that prevented me from speaking made me incapable of understanding the sounds . ... The effort of remembering each sound would have taken too much time, and conversation is far too cursive to permit the understanding of a sufficient number of words. ... Inwardly I felt the same as ever. This mental isolation which I mention, my sadness, my impediment and the appearance of stupidity which it gave rise to, led many to believe that my intellectual faculties were weakened. ... When I was alone and wide awake, I used to discuss within myself my life work and the studies I loved. ... My memory for facts, principles, dogmas, abstract ideas, was the same as when I enjoyed good health. Therefore, I could not believe myself ill; the impediments under which I suffered seemed to be no more than dreams (Riese and Hubert 1954, 238).

Lordat wrote that he would sit in his study for weeks looking at the papers he was writing before the disease declared itself but was unable to decipher written words. He lost syntax. But then, one day, he was sitting in his library when, like a camera pulling focus, the words on the spine of a book became crystal clear: "I could read exactly the title *Hippocratis Opera*. This discovery made tears of joy come to my eyes" (Riese and Hubert 1954, 238).

When Lordat recovered enough to write his own case notes, he extended his reflections to theorize about the relationship between language and thought. Of special consideration was the idea that language and intellect are one and inseparable, that language itself was the essence of human identity: intellect being the distinguishing characteristic of humanity. This was a prominent idea at the time Lordat was writing, in the 1840s. It was elaborated in the well-known writings of his contemporary Wilhelm von Humboldt. Language was not a symbolic representation of self, it was a direct expression of the inner self. Language was also physical; its functionality was located inside the brain. In a remarkable coincidence, just a few months before Lordat's aphasic episode, another French physician named Jean-Baptiste Bouillaud published a paper declaring that he had located "the legislative organ of speech" in a particular lobe of the brain, a claim that was to later inform both Paul Broca and Carl Wernicke.

What troubled Lordat was how his loss of words was seen by others, by definition, as a loss of *himself*, if one accepted the unity between language and intellect. For both a priest and a physician who identify themselves as following a vocation, a call from God to service humanity, their inner self was the same as their social or professional selves. In other words, Lordat's sense of self was defined as being a physician, not someone who during office hours assumes the role of a physician. Thus, what he was struggling to explain while trapped in splendid isolation, silenced by aphasia, was his ability to maintain his inner monologue while unable to speak or write a single medical term.

While Lordat was, by his own admission, able to have abstract thoughts, a more severe type of aphasia not only stifles language, but also cuts off comprehension; the words of others make no sense. It was with regard to this phenomenon, that, a half century after Lordat's accounts, philosophers and physicians turned their attention. A philosophical train of thought reduced the essence of human nature to abstract thought that was expressed to the world through language. Aphasic patients were interesting to philosophers and physicians alike because their pathology was somehow used as proof of something we cannot see. As with most biomedical investigations, the search for the normal way things must be is revealed through the scrutiny of the abnormal. In this case, the disappearance of language rendered visible the fragility of an inner, abstract thinking that made humans *themselves*. As neurologist Kurt Goldstein said of aphasia in 1940: "No other pathological material can teach us so much about the organization of the human being" (Goldstein 1940, 70).

The second half of the nineteenth century was an epoch of specialization of science, the very term "scientist" itself being introduced in 1833. The later decades saw an interesting conjunction of linguistics, neuroscience, philosophy, psychology, and neurosurgery, all of which drew on one another to identify the link between language and selfhood. It has even been suggested that it was precisely in the 1860s when the "aphasic patient" was created, meaning the diagnostic category, that medical literature established a set of conditions to define the illness. When patients who had aphasia following stroke died, their brains were dissected and areas of damage pinpointed, representing spots where ideas and words were located. (Figure 5) Diagrams were drawn to portray an underlying order to a chaotic mental status. For some, the objectification of disease separates the damaged part from the otherwise normal self. But sometimes images can be so seductive that it passes unnoticed that they provide only the façade of an answer to deeper questions about what has gone wrong with them.

A recent doctoral dissertation by Michael Anderson contained interviews with stroke patients and their families to investigate how they cope with recovery efforts. He quoted Mrs. Jenson as saying that when she was shown the scans of her husband's brain after his stroke, revealing bright spots of damage that affected his language and behavior, she was better able

280   THE DISORDERS OF SPEECH.

which are stored the motor memories which guide the right hand
in the act of writing.

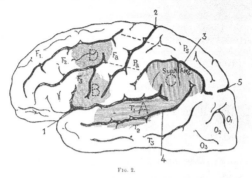

Fig. 2.

If, in the following manner (Fig. 3), we detach the four
centres from their connexions, and represent them as circles,

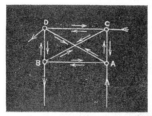

Fig. 3.

we shall be better able to indicate the relations of the four
to each other, and also their relations to incoming and outgoing
speech.

The exceedingly intimate relations of A and B have already
been commented upon: they are indicated by the connecting line
and the two arrows.   Without detailed discussion of the rela-

Figure 5: Diagram labeling parts of the brain corresponding to particular speech functions.
From John Wyllie (Edinburgh, 1894). Courtesy Wellcome Trust.

to come to terms with him not being "himself." The spots on the scan helped
her to conceptualize that his true self was severed, or "locked away," by the
diseased brain. Anderson stated that "This approach is something I often
encountered from the spouses, as they would assume that their 'former'
husband was still 'in there,' and argue that his real self would sometimes
emerge." However, this was not necessarily a view shared by the stroke

victims themselves, who "were often confused by how their spouses would reduce their selfhood to their brain and would have a hard time trying to deal with the othering of their spouse" (Anderson 2014, 152).

The way in which we talk about disease may have the unintended consequence of creating stigma and alienating the person experiencing the illness. An enormous amount of literature exploring medical narratives surrounding chronic illness, dementia, Parkinson's, and Alzheimer's, all point to the risks of using the wrong words to describe the condition. The psychologist and pioneer in patient-centered dementia studies, Tom Kitwood, described what he termed a "malignant social psychology" that destroys a patient's "personhood." We often hear of patients being subjected to a dual attack: once by the disease, and again by those who ridicule their symptoms. As Rik Cheston wrote, "The dominant story that is told about people with dementia is that their talk is meaningless, their memories are defective, and that their reminiscences are of little importance in the planning of care" (Cheston 1996, 598).

How people with cognitive impairment find adaptive ways to express themselves—for aphasic patients, what Kurt Goldstein called semantic "detours"—can itself be seen as pathological behavior. As Sabat and Harre wrote in their article "The Deconstruction of Self in Alzheimer's Disease,"

> If such behaviour is founded on story lines that paint the sufferer as inadequate, confused, helpless, etc., then that person will be so positioned and will have his or her behaviour interpreted by others in such a way as to *confirm* the initial story line and positioning. The ultimate result of such a situation is the fencing off of the sufferer so that no adequate self can be constructed. Perhaps it is not stretching the point too far to refer to such a situation as a species of self-fulfilling hypothesis (Sabat and Harre 1992, 460).

Losing speech appears to remove any defense against being seen by others as a diminished person. The neurologist John Hughlings Jackson wrote in 1874 that the aphasic patient had lost the power to "propositionize," meaning they lost the ability to make use of language because they lost the ability to think abstractly (Jackson 1915, 82). The speechless man had reverted to an equivalent *state of being* of "that of the little child which has been taught to understand speech, and has not yet spoken (Jackson 1915, 82)." The person was infantile, passive, defenseless.

Attempts to rehabilitate the person have historically resorted to facile assessments of mental capacity. In 1904 the Philadelphia neurologist Charles Mills wrote about his attempts to re-educate aphasic patients. He described a man who could not speak, did not comprehend numbers, but was not "word deaf" because he could follow instructions: "When he read aloud, he had a marked form of paraphasia, his speech being of the jargon or gibberish type. Like many such patients, he read off this jargon as if to himself he were reading correctly." (Mills 1904, 1944). The physician then describes himself as if he were a teacher or parent: "The education of the sensory aphasic is that of a child. ... we adopted what may be called the 'Mother's Method' ... we taught him to say *pa-pa* ... *ma-ma* ... then *wee wee*, and so on." This was to an adult who demonstrated comprehension but could not speak. We sense how unsettling this might be when recalling Lordat's fear of being perceived as an imbecile. Or, in this quotation from an aphasic woman who was in speech therapy and expressed her desperation to explain to people why she was not speaking to them: "I could not say the word 'stroke' ... I could not say that I had a stroke! And I had to learn how to say 'stroke' because I would say 'what happened to me'" (Nakano 2005, 50).

The rehabilitation of aphasic patients is a highly challenging undertaking. One conventional measure of progress would be in the degree of recovery of speech. But if that is not happening, an assessment of the patient's sense of well-being is important. How does one think about being well? Quality of life is a concept that was developed in the 1940s to assess a person's functional capacity, that is, their ability to perform physical tasks. It gained currency in the 1970s and became the epitome of qualitative health research when questionnaires were developed purportedly eliciting the patient's perspective on their own progress in health recovery. There are over a thousand validated quality-of-life instruments today assessing whether patients feel better following a specific intervention. It is a measure of therapeutic effectiveness that traces a continuum of patienthood. But the measure is often criticized for having no standardized definition of "quality" in the phrase "quality of life." These instruments produce exact numbers on a scale that refer to nothing specific.

Currently, there are efforts to produce quality-of-life instruments for aphasic patients, the obvious challenge being that sometimes the patient cannot reply. There is an initiative called "Back to the Drawing Board," through which cartoons are drawn for patients who possess graphic comprehension to generate stories. Some patients with Broca's aphasia, who can comprehend but not speak words, *are able* to gesture and even learn sign language (Morgan and Helm-Estabrooks 1987, 64-72). In the 1970s, a "Pantomime Recognition Test" was developed in which actors imitated the use of objects, and patients were asked to point to drawings of objects corresponding to the performance, such as a comb (R. Duffy, J. Duffy, and Pearson 1975, 115-132). However, it has been shown that deaf people who primarily use sign language can also lose that function from aphasia (Damasio et al. 1986, 363-365). Similarly, those with Wernicke's aphasia, showing comprehension deficit, also might be unable to understand gestures. There are theories of differential language acquisition processes using cases of bilingual patients, earlier called polyglots, who lose use of their secondary language more severely than their primary one (Kuzmina et al. 2019). The idea is that the first language is hard-wired to your brain and more resistant to damage. This all suggests possible different cognitive processes at work in establishing a means of communication that might lead to new areas of speech therapy. If successful, one would hope that the questions being posed by the health care team about quality of life, or sense of being, are the questions the patient wants to answer. We should not leave in silence what the aphasic patient might want to, but cannot, say.

Clinical assessments for aphasic patients who cannot self-report are immensely challenging. If communication is severely compromised, how is there any way of knowing what a person is thinking? How do you know if they can even talk to themselves? How do you know if they are internally debating the pros and cons of an action? Multiple theories have been put forth as to whether inner speech is dependent on outer speech comprehension, the ability to understand words presented to them (Geva et al. 2011, 323-343). However, it is extremely difficult to conduct research in this area, not least because if a patient apparently cannot comprehend written or spoken words, with Wernicke's aphasia, then they cannot offer informed consent. There is an increased risk of therapeutic misconception, and of consenting to research that has no direct benefits to the patient, such as undergoing brain scans to confirm a site lesion (Penn et al. 2009, 3-32). Given that there are variable degrees of severity of aphasia, it's recognized in the affected community that informed consent is a process and not a document.

By way of conclusion, I want to remind us that the word "disease" means dis-ease, not being at ease with oneself. From the patient's point of view, they are suffering not because of a thing that can be named, measured, or surgically removed, but because they no longer feel like themselves. Suffering loss of language is, I think, particularly challenging because of a deeply-rooted cultural conditioning that claims language is more than a tool that might fracture; it is the essential connection between the inner self and the world around us. When studying the grief response to language loss, two speech neuropathologists, Tanner and Gerstenberger, put it this way: "a person's psychological status cannot be separated from the neuropathology of speech and language" (Tanner and Gerstenberger 1988, 79-84).

A psychiatrist named Scott Moss had a stroke that resulted in aphasia. As a clinician, he was compulsive enough to document the course of his recovery: he recorded many of his therapy sessions and conversations and wrote a book about his experience in 1972. He said that when he woke up in the hospital, "I could understand vaguely what others said to me if it was spoken slowly ... I had lost completely the ability to talk, to read, and to write. I even lost for the first two months the ability to use words internally, that is, in my thinking. ... I had also lost the ability to dream. ... I lived in a total vacuum of self-produced concepts" (Moss 1972, 5).

Did he cease to exist? If one cannot self-talk, if one cannot comprehend the symbolism of communication or think abstractly, if one cannot dream, what is the state of being? For those looking at the person, is it possible to empathize with that experience? Can you put yourself in that person's place and imagine what the experience is like? When the philosopher Ludwig Wittgenstein was a student at Cambridge University, his Russian instructor underwent a tonsillectomy and was recovering in the hospital. When Wittgenstein visited her and asked how she felt, she replied: "just like a dog that had been run over." Wittgenstein considered her comment, and then said: "You don't know what a dog that has been run over feels like" (C. Elliott and B. Elliott 1991, 173). This was less a joke than a compulsive criticism over a choice of metaphor. It relates to the central idea behind his later work that philosophical problems arise from the misuse of the logic of language. It exposes weaknesses in how we think about the relationship between words and reality, part of the analytical "linguistic turn" in Anglo-American philosophy that occurred in the early-twentieth century. The pathology of losing language may not actually reveal the normality of narrative ways of being, but may lead us to wonder whether we have simply created a fiction of ourselves.

Our attention to the patient's point of view – approached through narrative medicine, life stories, illness, autobiography – has aimed to amplify the voice of those who suffer. Yet, in our efforts to privilege the patient's perspective, these methods may inadvertently assert hegemony over non-narrative frameworks of being.

The disciplines of history of science and medicine have long sought to explain how investigators try to make sense of the unknown, and how data derived by experimenters reflects the construction of the instruments designed to ask certain questions of nature (Clarke and Fujimura, 1992). In the interdisciplinary fields of science and technology studies (STS), such theories of representational practice have grown from philosophical notions of "theory-laden observation," suggesting that there is no such thing as "pure" empirical data; even the act of looking at something, an act considered unimpeachable because of the direct connection between perception and what is being perceived, is contaminated by *preconceptions*, by "filters" and "lenses" (whether literal or figurative) (Daston 2008). In much the same way that these studies have challenged our historical reliance on instruments and vision, this chapter asks that we think of language not as an unproblematic connection to the world, but as a tool shaped by theories and preconceptions that interfere with our understanding of how people might otherwise connect with the world. Just as Dr. Jill Taylor expressed in the account raised earlier in this chapter, the removal of language through stroke removed the "perceived boundaries" that had shaped her life experience.

Thoughts about the role of communication in identity formation are not exclusive to the domain of linguistics, neuroscience, or philosophy. It is a multi-disciplinary discussion that has yet to answer soul-searching questions that patients often have when struck with stroke. Perhaps it is so individualized that no dictates of natural science or biomedicine can be said to speak for all, another fictional narrative. But I do think that reflecting on the abnormality of the condition might offer new insights into how we normally talk about living with illness or states of well-being.

Works Cited

Anderson, Michael. 2014. "A Question of Location - Life with Fatigue After Stroke." PhD, diss., University of Copenhagen.

Charmaz, Kathy. 1983. "Loss of Self: A Fundamental Form of Suffering in the Chronically Ill." *Sociology of Health & Illness* 5, no. 2: 168–95. https://doi.org/10.1111/1467-9566.ep10491512.

Cheston, Rik. 1996. "Stories and Metaphors: Talking about the Past in a Psychotherapy Group for People with Dementia." *Ageing and Society* 16, no. 5: 579–602. https://doi.org/10.1017/S0144686X00020249.

Clarke, Adele and Joan Fujimura. 1992. *The Right Tools for the Job: At Work in Twentieth-Century Life Sciences*. Princeton: Princeton University Press.

Damasio, Antonio R., Ursula Bellugi, Hanna Damasio, Howard Poizner, and John Van Gilder. 1986. "Sign Language Aphasia during Left-Hemisphere Amytal Injection." *Nature* 322, no. 6077: 363–65. https://doi.org/10.1038/322363a0.

Daston, Lorraine. 2008. "On Scientific Observation." *Isis* 99, no. 1: 97-110.

Duffy, Robert J., Joseph R. Duffy, and Karen Leiter Pearson. 1975. "Pantomime Recognition in Aphasics." *Journal of Speech and Hearing Research* 18, no. 1: 115–32. https://doi.org/10.1044/jshr.1801.115.

Elliott, Carl, and Britt Elliott. 1991. "From the Patient's Point of View: Medical Ethics and the Moral Imagination." *Journal of Medical Ethics* 17, no. 4: 173–78. https://doi.org/10.1136/jme.17.4.173

Gallagher, Shaun. 2000. "Philosophical Conceptions of the Self: Implications for Cognitive Science." *Trends in Cognitive Sciences* 4, no. 1:

14–21. https://doi.org/10.1016/S1364-6613(99)01417-5.

Geva, Sharon, Sophie Bennett, Elizabeth A. Warburton, and Karalyn Patterson. 2011. "Discrepancy between Inner and Overt Speech: Implications for Post-Stroke Aphasia and Normal Language Processing." *Aphasiology* 25, no. 3: 323–343. https://doi.org/10.1080/02687038.2010.511236.

Goldstein, Kurt. 1940. *Human Nature in the Light of Psychopathology: The William James Lecture.* Cambridge, MA: Harvard University Press.

Henderson, Victor W. 1990. "Alalia, Aphemia, and Aphasia." *Archives of Neurology* (Chicago) 47, no. 1: 85–88. https://doi.org/10.1001/archneur.1990.00530010107028.

Hinojosa, Ramon, Craig Boylstein, Maude Rittman, Melanie Sberna Hinojosa, and Christopher A. Faircloth. 2008. "Constructions of Continuity after Stroke." *Symbolic Interaction* 31, no. 2: 205–24. https://doi.org/10.1525/si.2008.31.2.205.

Jackson, John Hughlings. 1915. "On The Nature Of The Duality Of The Brain." *Brain* (London, England: 1878) 38, no. 1–2: 80–86. https://doi.org/10.1093/brain/38.1-2.80

Jacyna, L.S. 2009. *Lost Words: Narratives of Language and the Brain, 1825-1926.* Princeton: Princeton University Press.

Kaufman, Sharon. 1988. "Illness, Biography, and the Interpretation of Self Following a Stroke." *Journal of Aging Studies* 2, no. 3: 217–27. https://doi.org/10.1016/0890-4065(88)90002-3.

Kaufman, Sharon R. 2017. "'Losing My Self': A Poet's Ironies and a Daughter's Reflections on Dementia." *Perspectives in Biology and Medicine* 60, no. 4: 549–68. https://doi.org/10.1353/pbm.2017.0042.

Ethan Kross, Emma Bruehlman-Senecal, Jiyoung Park, Aleah Burson, Adrienne Dougherty, Holly Shablack, Ryan Bremner, Jason Moser, and Ozlem Ayduk. 2014. "Self-Talk as a Regulatory Mechanism: How You Do It Matters." *Journal of Personality and Social Psychology* 106, no. 2:

304–24.

Kuzmina, Ekaterina, Mira Goral, Monica Norvik, and Brendan S. Weekes. 2019. "What Influences Language Impairment in Bilingual Aphasia? A Meta-Analytic Review." *Frontiers in Psychology* 10: 445. https://doi.org/10.3389/fpsyg.2019.00445.

Lordat, Jacques. 1843. "Analyse de la parole pour servir à la théorie de divers cas d'ALALIE et de PARALALIE (de mutisme et d'imperfection du parler) que les Nosologistes ont mal connus." *Journal de la Société de Médecine Pratique de Montpellier* 7: 417–433.

Mills, Charles K. 1904. "Treatment Of Aphasia By Training." *Journal of the American Medical Association* XLIII, no. 26: 1940–1949. https://doi.org/10.1001/jama.1904.92500260002d.

Morgan, Alisa, and Nancy Helm-Estabrooks. 1987. "Back to the Drawing Board: A Treatment Program for Nonverbal Aphasic Patients." *Clinical Aphasiology* 17: 64–72.

Moser, Jason S., Adrienne Dougherty, Whitney I. Mattson, Benjamin Katz, Tim P. Moran, Darwin Guevarra, Holly Shablack, Ozlem Ayduk, John Jonides, Marc G. Berman, and Ethan Kross. 2017. "Third-Person Self-Talk Facilitates Emotion Regulation without Engaging Cognitive Control: Converging Evidence from ERP and FMRI." *Scientific Reports* 7, no. 1: 1–9. https://doi.org/10.1038/s41598-017-04047-3.

Moss, C. Scott. 1972. *Recovery with Aphasia: The Aftermath of My Stroke.* Champaign, IL: University of Illinois Press.

Nakano, Erline. 2005. "Changes in the Perception and Sense of Self of Individuals With Aphasia: An Ethnographic Study." M.S. Thesis, University of South Florida. https://digitalcommons.usf.edu/etd/785/.

Penn, Claire, Tali Frankel, Jennifer Watermeyer, and Madeleine Müller. 2009. "Informed Consent and Aphasia: Evidence of Pitfalls

in the Process." *Aphasiology* 23, no. 1: 3–32. https://doi.
org/10.1080/02687030701521786.

Riese, Walther, and Judd Hubert. 1954. "Auto-Observation of Aphasia:
Reported by an Eminent Nineteenth Century Medical Scientist."
Bulletin of the History of Medicine 28, no. 3: 237–42.

Sabat, Steven R., and Rom Harré. 1992. "The Construction and
Deconstruction of Self in Alzheimer's Disease." *Ageing and Society* 12,
no. 4: 443–61. https://doi.org/10.1017/S0144686X00005262.

Smith, R. 1992. *Inhibition: History and Meaning in the Sciences of Mind and
Brain.* Berkeley, CA: University of California Press.

Tanner, Dennis C., and Dean L. Gerstenberger. 1988. "The Grief
Response in Neuropathologies of Speech and Language." *Aphasiology*
2, no. 1: 79–84. https://doi.org/10.1080/02687038808248889.

Taylor, Jill Bolte. 2008. *My Stroke of Insight: A Brain Scientist's Personal Journey.*
New York, NY: Viking Press.

3

The Construction of Affect in Narratives of Chronic Disease Experiences

Mariana Pascual, *Pontificia Universidad Católica de Chile*

Abstract:

Most studies on health discourse have focused on doctor-patient communication. However, analyses describing other types of interaction are scarce and may be revealing in terms of how chronic patients perceive themselves and their relationship with the condition. Our focus is on endometriosis, a gynecological chronic condition affecting one out of ten women worldwide. This chapter presents a study conducted to determine (1) how language is used to construct meanings of affect in narratives of endometriosis experiences by Spanish-speaking women from Chile across genre and (2) what entities they appraise. The corpus comprises data from two genres: Facebook comments collected from open-access pages for endometriosis patients, and autobiographical narratives collected in open interviews. A mixed-methods approach was used. A qualitative analysis was implemented based on an adapted version of the interpersonal system of Appraisal within Systemic Functional Linguistics (SFL); the quantitative analysis was conducted to determine differences across genres and tendencies regarding the entities on which patients focus their positive and negative affect. The results indicate that patients show a clear preference for the use of meanings associated to un/happiness, which relate to lasting feelings of sadness, construed explicitly or in an implicit manner. Statistical results show some significant differences across genres, which may help understand the meanings construed in health communication. The results shed light on some relevant issues that should be considered in medical humanities to reach a more comprehensive understanding of patients, who are seldom heard beyond the context of healthcare institutions. This understanding may, in turn, help improve the seriously impoverished life-quality that characterizes patients with chronic pain.

The Role of Language in Healthcare

The value of language and its impact on a patient's health is unquestionable (Bukstein 2016) and cannot be underestimated. For a long time, we have known that patients' attitudes towards their conditions, their doctors, and their treatments are impacted by personal and cultural beliefs (Shahin, Kennedy, and Stupans 2019) as well as by the quality of their interactions with other social actors (Bañón Hernández 2018). From a discourse analytical perspective, most studies on health communication have focused on one specific form of interaction: doctor-patient communication (e.g., Wodak 1997; Braghetto and Baronti 2007; Bonnin 2013). As social individuals who have been involved in this type of interaction, most of us are aware of the constraints imposed by time limitations and by the knowledge and, in consequence, power asymmetries of this type of communication, to mention just a few of the several personal and institutional factors that shape this form of interaction.

Analyses describing other types of health communication are not as common, though they may be revealing in terms of how chronic patients perceive themselves and their relationship with the condition they suffer. Over the last years, my research has focused on endometriosis, a chronic gynecological condition affecting one out of ten women worldwide (see, e.g., Pascual 2020; 2021; Pascual and Diaz Alegría 2021). It is a condition that, in most cases, causes debilitating pain and, eventually, a strong effect on patients' quality of life and can even impact their mental health (Laganà et al. 2017; Bullo 2018; Hållstam et al. 2018; Facchin et al. 2015). Another aspect of endometriosis that is highly relevant is that it accounts for nearly half the number of infertility cases, and this fact is closely related to delays in diagnosis (Fauconnier et al. 2021), which can and should be prevented.

Some authors have focused specifically on endometriosis patients' narratives. Bullo (2018) described how women who suffer endometriosis become disempowered by their chronic condition. Koller and Bullo (2019) identified the function of certain semiotic elements, such as tattoos, in the construction of identity in the case of women who live with the disease. Another resource that has been studied in the literature is the use of metaphors, which has proved to be a valuable and recurrent meaning-making tool for the linguistic construction of pain and painful experiences (Bullo 2018; Bullo and Hearn 2020; Pascual 2020). Previous studies have also demonstrated that emotions play a fundamental role in patients' discourse and that the dimension of affect is of utmost importance in patient-patient interaction (Pascual 2020; 2021; Pascual and Díaz Alegría 2021).

Over the last years, my research has been conducted in the context of the Project 11190133 *Discourse and health: The discourse construction of pain in patients with chronic diseases*, funded by ANID, the National Chilean Research Agency. I have attempted to contribute to an understanding of the role that situated, contextualized language (discourse) plays in health communication, with the ultimate purpose of understanding what patients who suffer chronic pain go through and providing some guidelines for better communication. This essay presents results from my studies regarding the following aspects: (1) how language is used to construct affect in narratives relating endometriosis experiences of Spanish-speaking women from Chile across discourse genres, and (2) what entities these patients evaluate in their narratives, i.e. what are the objects of their evaluations. Once those questions are answered, we may reach a better understanding of what they feel, what they care about, and what they worry about.

The theoretical bases on which my research is grounded include a combination of functional views that support the perspective of language as a socio-semiotic resource for creating meaning (Halliday 1978; Halliday 2004). This perspective and the role that functional approaches assign to actual instances of language use is essential when analyzing genuine data to shed light on social phenomena and determine how the language operates to reconstruct them.

The results that I present here have emerged from the analysis of two different corpora, which correspond to two discourse genres. In line with the theoretical perspective adopted, I define a genre as a "staged, goal-oriented purposeful activity in which speakers engage as members of our culture" (Martin 1985). This social perspective of genre implies a strong emphasis on the integral role that context plays in the meaning-making process. This is always a fundamental aspect in discourse studies, but it is particularly so under certain conditions, as in the case of oral communication, in which multiple contextual factors operate in the semiosis, apart from the literal meanings conveyed by the language itself.

My data derives from Facebook comments collected from open-access pages for endometriosis patients, and from autobiographical narratives collected in open interviews. In all cases, I will refer to data produced by Chilean women of reproductive age, who have been diagnosed with endometriosis, and who have produced their discourses in natural instances. In the Facebook comments, the pages were open-access, and in the case of the interviews, the patients volunteered to participate in the study, which was, in their view, a way of making their condition more visible.

I consider an eclectic methodology to be the most suitable way to approach this data, and that is the reason for using a mixed-methods approach (Creswell et al. 2003; Teddlie and Tashakkori 2011). A qualitative analysis was implemented based on an adapted version of the interpersonal system of Appraisal (Martin 2000; Martin and White 2005; Ngo and Unsworth 2015) within Systemic Functional Linguistics (SFL) (Halliday 1978; Halliday 2004). The quantitative analysis was conducted to determine differences across genres and tendencies regarding the entities on which the patients focus their positive and negative affect.

In the next sections, I will attempt to shed light on some relevant issues that should be considered in the medical humanities to reach a more comprehensive understanding of patients whose voices are seldom heard beyond the context of healthcare institutions. This understanding may, in turn, help improve the seriously impoverished quality of life that characterizes patients with chronic pain.

How Spanish-Speaking Women from Chile Use Language to Construct Affect: Focusing on the Discourse Genre Factor

For centuries, medical practice involved a segmented interpretation of the subject, focusing almost exclusively on biological aspects of health. With the advent of new paradigms in healthcare, and thanks to the emergence and rapid expansion of the medical humanities (Sánchez González 2017), more integral and comprehensive views were incorporated into the education and training of health professionals. One of the new elements of the wholistic perspectives is the acknowledgment of patients' voice, not as a mere indicator of their organic situation, but as a means to unveil the presence of other factors that may be playing a part, and sometimes a very important one, in the general condition of the patient.

To contribute to a deeper understanding of patients and their narratives, we explored endometriosis patients' experiences in two discourse genres.

The definition of genre to which we adhere is the one proposed by Martin (2009), who defines it as "a recurrent configuration of meanings" (13) and "a staged, goal-oriented social process" (Martin and Rose 2007, 8). This implies that under different cultural and situational circumstances, speakers produce different configurations of meanings, and different text types, which are predictable for speakers of a given culture.

The choice of Facebook comments was grounded on the need to capture the patients' discourses in genuine interaction with other patients, thus canceling out the impact of power/knowledge asymmetries characteristic of other types of interaction. Open-access Facebook pages also proved to offer room for open dialogue, enabling the free expression of certain topics that are not usually incorporated in doctor-patient communication. The pages selected for analysis met all of the following criteria: they were open access; were of explicit Chilean origin; were on endometriosis (main subject); and had a minimum of 750 followers to ensure a reasonable volume of data. The three pages that were selected were: *Fuchen*[1] (*Fundación Chilena de Endometriosis*), *Endo Chile*,[2] and *Endometriosis en Chile*.[3] All pages were operational during the period under analysis, which ranged from January 2016 to March 2020. The initial data corresponded to their simultaneous formal operations, as registered on the platform, and the end of data collection was determined by the onset of the COVID-19 pandemic. Because these Facebook pages were constituted for health-related purposes, emerging discussions related to COVID-19 could have overwhelmed the pages' earlier focus on endometriosis, and so data collection ended with the emergence of COVID-19.

Linguistic and non-linguistic data were initially collected. The latter

1. https://www.facebook.com/search/top?q=fundaci%C3%B3n%20chilena%20de%20 endometriosis
2. https://www.facebook.com/search/top?q=endo%20chi
3. https://www.facebook.com/EndometriosisEnChile

consisted mainly of graphs, emojis, gifs, and other semiotic resources typical of social media (Stæhr 2015). For the purposes of our research, only linguistic data were analyzed. The unit of analysis for this corpus was the Facebook comment produced by the patient participating in the platform interaction, referring to some aspect of her condition. The corpus comprised a total of 3,057 comments (69,944 words). This number corresponds to the resulting number of words retrieved by Ncapture, the Nvivo tool for capturing web data. It does not include emoticons or numeric data.

For the interviews, we captured the autobiographical narratives (Harvey and Koteyko 2012) of thirty Chilean women, all Spanish speakers of reproductive age, with a formal, institutional diagnosis of endometriosis. The women who were interviewed volunteered to participate in the study, responding to a call that was distributed on social media. Due to the COVID-19 sanitary restrictions at that time, all interviews were conducted online, using Zoom, Meet, or WhatsApp video calls. They were conducted during April and March of 2021 and ranged in duration from 30 to 45 minutes each, with an average of 39.6 minutes. The total recording time was 19.53 hours. All interviews were recorded and transcribed. The resulting corpus is made up of a total of 180,159 words. All names of participants, other social actors (such as physicians, nurses, and other health personnel), locations, and institutions have been modified in the transcribed versions to protect the participants' integrity and anonymity. Apart from signing the ethics consent for participation, the women interviewed had to be Chilean or live in Chile and speak Spanish as their native language, be officially diagnosed with the condition by a licensed practitioner, and be of reproductive age.

Table 1 summarizes the characteristics of the informants who participated in the interviews.[4]

4. The study received the ethical approval of PUC Ethical Committee with reference number 20210111.

Number of participants	30
Age range; median	23-47; 34
Occupation	Homemaker, university student, sociologist (2), hairdresser, nurse, independent worker (4), teacher (7), reporter (2), chemist, social worker, anthropologist, psychologist (2), engineer (2), transcriber, computer analyst, and accountant
Years since diagnosis; median	1-24; 6
Level of education	Completed secondary education = 4 Completed technical higher education = 5 University student = 1 University graduate = 20
Number of surgeries	None = 12 One surgery = 14 More than one = 4

Table 1. Description of the women who were interviewed for the study.

The purpose of our analysis was to determine whether the attitudinal meanings of affect that they produced varied across genres (Pascual 2021; Pascual and Díaz Alegría 2021). Attitudinal meanings are those "concerned with our feelings, including emotional reactions, judgements of behaviour and evaluation of things" (Martin and White 2005, 35). In this model, the semantic domain of attitude is subdivided into affect, judgment, and appreciation. Affect refers to the resources that language offers to create emotional reactions; judgment refers to how we assess people and their behavior, based on sociocultural norms, while the dimension of appreciation is concerned with the resources that are used to construct the value of objects, processes, and phenomena.

The theoretical and analytical proposal on which we based our study considers four domains of affect: un/happiness, dis/satisfaction, dis/inclination and in/security. All the data from the two corpora were manually categorized with the use of software (Nvivo New 2020) to assist in the handling and processing of data. The analysis included the identification of the following categories: type of affect realization (direct or indirect/metaphorical); appraised entity (i.e. object, person or concept being evaluated or triggering the affect); polarity (positive or negative affect); and type of affect constructed. Affect types were classified following the original proposal in the System of Appraisal (Martin 2000; Martin and White 2005), with dimensions and subdimensions that are presented and illustrated in Table 2. It is important to note that dis/inclination refers to dimensions of affect emerging from *irrealis*, possible future scenarios (such as feelings of fear or desire that result from something that may happen), whereas the other dimensions constitute affective reactions to real entities, as evaluated by the speaker.

Type	Sub-type	Example
Dis/inclination	Desire	Me gustaría que alguna institución me ayudara (I'd like some institution to help me).
	Fear	Tengo miedo de que me dejen peor de lo que estoy. (I'm afraid they're going to leave me worse than I am).
Un/happiness	Cheer	Ando de muy buen ánimo. (I'm in a very good mood).
	Antipathy	Los médicos se burlan de uno. (Doctors make fun of you).
	Misery	Lamentablemente el tiempo pasó. (Unfortunately, it's too late).
	Affection	Un afectuoso saludo desde Penco. (Warm greetings from Penco).
Dis/satisfaction	Interest	Quiero saber eso. (I want to know that).
	Pleasure	Gracias a ella llegué a un especialista. (Thanks to her I got to a specialist).
	Ennui	Ya estaba agotada de todo. (I was already exhausted by everything).
	Displeasure	Hace años vengo aceptándolo para no deprimirme. (I've been coming to terms with it for years to avoid depression).

In/security	Confidence	Tengo alguna esperanza de no sentir más dolor. (I have some hope of feeling no more pain).
	Trust	Me siento más tranquila estando en sus manos (I feel more at ease in his hands).
	Surprise	Estoy de un par de semanas y aún no lo creo. (I'm a couple of weeks [pregnant] and I still can't believe it).
	Disquiet	Estoy muy desorientada respecto al tema. (I am very confused on the subject).

Table 2. Affect: types and subtypes (adapted from Martin and White 2005) with examples from our corpora.

The analysis of the Facebook comments pointed to un/happiness as the prevailing type of affect that endometriosis patients constructed in their discourse. This feeling accounted for 39 percent of all instances identified. In descending order, the other categories represented 31 percent for dis/satisfaction, 21 percent for dis/inclination, and 9 percent for in/security. The prevailing domain of un/happiness comprises four areas: misery and antipathy for unhappiness, and cheer and affection for happiness. A closer look into the instances revealed that, by far, the highest value corresponded to misery. The following extract illustrates the profound sadness experienced by the patient, in which she writes:

Me encantaria conocieran mi caso necesito ayuda quiero ser madre y no se si podre lograrlo ya tengo 37 años y me afecto mi sistema reproductor me operaron y estoy profundamente agradecida pero la infertilidad el sistema publico no tiene recursos para ayudarnos me gustaria q alguna institucion me ayudara es muy triste no poder ser madre (I'd like you to know my case. I need help. I want to be a mother and I don't know if I'll be able to. I'm already 37 and it has affected my reproductive system. I went through surgery, and I am profoundly grateful but the infertility, the public system has no resources to help us. I'd like some institution to help me. Not being able to be a mother is so sad.)[5]

Descriptions corresponding to this domain of affect include indirect expressions that encode experiences interpreted as profoundly sad, by activating context, even when the word "sad" or related lexical items do not encode this feeling, as can be observed in the following example:

Yo ya pase x cuatro cirugías, años tirada en la cama c mucho dolor, y los médicos me mandaban a una sicólogo, ya no tengo ningún órgano reproductivo, me la paso c calmantes y hormonas que destruyen mi cuerpo y mis ganas d seguir... (I've already been through four surgeries, years lying in bed in pain and the doctors kept sending me to see a psychologist, I no longer have my reproductive organs, and I'm always taking painkillers and hormones that destroy my body and my willingness to continue.)

These narratives construct feelings of sadness, emerging from a variety of reasons, which will be dealt with in the next section. In any case, this is a highly enlightening finding, since it shows a realm of meaning that is unlikely to arise in other types of interaction, such as during a medical consultation. When we turn our attention to a different discourse genre, the interviews, the results are not optimistic.

---

5. All examples have been transcribed in their original format. As a result, errors may be found in grammar, spelling, and typology. It may be observed that in some ways, this lack of care for the form resembles a form of think-aloud or free flow of consciousness, typical of digital communication in which the patient pays close attention to meaning. In a way, this style is closer to oral than to written interaction.

It is noteworthy that the fact that this interaction was digitally mediated had a strong impact on the comments' functionality. Though it might be reasonable to expect Facebook comments in which patients focused on their own needs to recount their experiences with the pathology, and, by doing so, construct their emotions in the comments, the main functionality was found to be more closely associated with other purposes, more closely related to construing and maintaining a sense of community through this digital platform. The following comments illustrate this idea:

> gracias a sus publicaciones he dado a conocer nuestra enfermedad en nuestro entorno !! (thanks to your publications I have made our disease known in our environment!!)

> gracias a ella llegue a un especialista, gracias a la página por orientarme en muchas dudas que tenía (thanks to her I got to a specialist, thanks to the page for guiding me in many doubts I had)

The use of digital platforms seems to have created the grounds for a new form of information generation and exchange, which, in the past, took place in support groups for people who went through some traumatic situation, such as the loss of a loved one, or the suffering of a serious disease or addiction. Typical examples include the traditional church support groups for people affected by alcohol or drug abuse, soldiers with post-traumatic syndromes, parents who have lost their children, and cancer patients, among others. Such communities were formed out of the need to share their experiences, with a strong focus on the healing power of narrative, which also constitutes the basis for psychological practice and the foundations for narrative medicine (Charon et al. 2017). Belonging to a community of shared interests, even in the case of shared suffering, offers most individuals a feeling of relief. The internet offers fertile soil for the emergence of these groups, and they seem to be genuinely helpful, as reported by their members (for a detailed report of the functionality of support groups on Facebook see Pascual 2020).

For the interviews, a similar distribution of affect dimensions was found. Un/happiness was the prevailing dimension, followed by in/satisfaction, dis/inclination and in/security. The main difference was observed in the occurrence of these meanings. The percentage for un/happiness was 51 percent, a very high percentage, followed by 29 percent in/satisfaction, 13 percent for dis/inclination and 6 percent for in/security. Below is an example of how unhappiness was constructed in the interviews:

… es difícil describirlo porque es como: | es como un desgarro | | eh: | pero inhabilitante es una cuestión: que no no te permite: em: | moverte o sea pa mí era un: | era una cuestión absolutamente inhabilitante no puedes pensar ni hacer otra cosa más que | eh: | estar centrado en en en aguantar y que pase | que el dolor pase no hay posibilidad de: | de pensar en otra cosa de hacer otra cosa nada más que | que pase este momento cachai (… it's difficult to describe because it's like: | it's like a tear | | eh: | but disabling it's something that doesn't let you: em: | move that is to me it was a: | it was something completely disabling you cannot think or do anything else but | eh: | but concentrate on on holding on and wait for it to pass | for the pain to go away there's no possibility to: | to think of anything else or do anything else just wait for that moment to pass | you see?)

Several patients codified how they felt in the form of a bodily reaction. This is a very explicit social way to understand how serious and unbearable the sensation is, even when they make no explicit linguistic reference, as can be seen in the following example:

… yo una vez me acuerdo que me tiré en el baño en posición fetal y estuve ahí no sé cuánto rato tirada y no me podía mover no podía | no había nadie no podía pedir ayuda no podía tomarme algo no podía ir a buscar algo | y es como | que pase esta huevada por favor >que pase que pase que pase. (I remember once that I threw myself in the bathroom in a fetal position and I was lying there for I don't know how long and I couldn't move I couldn't | no one was there I couldn't ask for help I couldn't take a pill I couldn't go get something | and it's like | let this shit go away please > just go away, go away, go away.)

Our analysis of both corpora indicates a clear tendency for women to represent how unhappy their experiences were. Patients show a strong preference for the use of meanings that relate to lasting feelings of sadness, construed in either an explicit or an implicit manner. Showing sympathy and acting towards improving their life quality should constitute an aim of everyone involved in their healthcare.

What Do Women Who Have Experienced Endometriosis Care About and Worry About?

In this section, the focus turns from the patients' feelings towards the referential semiotic elements, people, processes, and even propositions or proposals that they construct in their discourse and also appraise. Being able to identify their worries and concerns will make it possible to understand them from a more holistic perspective. Though this may be true of any health condition, in the case of gynecological illnesses, it becomes particularly relevant.

It is always important to place the patient at the center of our healthcare system. The long tradition of patient-centered medical humanities (Dolan 2015) has paved the way for other researchers. Our contribution places women at the center of the scene who have suffered not only the power asymmetries of traditional healthcare systems and doctor-patient interaction (Pascual 2020), but also the consequences of being socially silenced for centuries in male-dominated cultures. This situation brings to light another negative contributing factor, which is the gynecological nature of the disease, traditionally associated with taboo topics in Latino cultures. Menstrual pain has been silenced and normalized for centuries (Rubinsky, Gunning, and Cooke-Jackson 2018; Hennegan et al. 2021), and this sociocultural phenomenon has worsened the experience of endometriosis, delaying diagnosis, with irreversible impacts on women's fertility in a high number of cases (Hudelist et al. 2012).

Infertility is a common association when referring to endometriosis. But is this what patients really worry about? The results from our studies indicate otherwise. In all cases, and due to methodological constraints, the entity that they mention most frequently in their discourse is endometriosis. It is the most productive category, associated with a great variety of negative as well as positive types of affect. They mention it in relation to unhappiness and dissatisfaction, but also when they refer to their hopes and expectations. One of the subcategories of endometriosis is the diagnosis, which plays a fundamental role. The most frequent situation that the interviewed women narrate refers to getting a diagnosis after several consultations in which they felt ignored, and their pain was systematically normalized, time after time. Therefore, "putting a name" to what they experienced is usually a cause of relief.

The literature has reported that women with endometriosis achieve a sense of empowerment from having obtained a diagnosis (Bullo 2018), and, in general, access to information related to the condition that they suffer is highly valued and appreciated. In line with the literature, we observed that information, in the form of a diagnosis, is frequently constructed as a valuable, though rare, social value to achieve, as may be observed in the following extract:

nada hasta que nada la ginecóloga con la que fui ese año | en realidad cuando me dijo como qué era lo que tenía | igual como que me alivié mucho | este hecho de saber como que no era lo que yo tenía | como que solamente yo sabía que sufría y cada vez que me llegaba la regla yo me ponía a llorar como | de angustia (nothing until the gynecologist I went with that year | actually when she told me what I had like | just as I was relieved | this fact of knowing how it was not what I had | like only I knew how much I was suffering and every time I got my period I started to cry like | out of anguish).

Lack of information is frequently associated with the gynecologists' lack of empathy and genuine concern. It is not unusual to read how much suffering these women had to go through until someone eventually paid real attention to them. One of our interviewees voices this:

iba al doctor una vez al año a hacer los chequeos que hay que hacerse ginecológicos y: | y me decía bueno: cómo son tus reglas yo le decía | me duele lo que me duran me duelen | hay unas que me duelen mucho más que otras | pero jamás | diciendo oye | ¿sabi qué? a veces me dan ganas de agarrarme a cabezazos con las murallas del dolor | ¿cachai? (I went to the doctor once a year for the gynecological check-ups and: | and he told me well: how are your periods I told him | they hurt they hurt | there are some that hurt much more than others | but never | saying hey | you know what? sometimes it makes me want to bang my head against the walls because of the pain | you see?)

Other entities that were associated with their condition included economic factors. In Chile, as in several other Latin American countries, having to resort to the public health system is considered a form of "social punishment," a price to pay for being poor. Private health in this country is limited to those who can afford a very high monthly cost, and beneficiaries of the private system only account for 14 percent of the population. Social inequalities and the lack of choice emerged systematically from the corpora. Mentions usually referred to lengthy periods, usually several months, before managing to see a health professional, and a similar situation before being able to get an appointment for a surgical procedure. If the patients have access to the private sector, they must pay extremely high costs. Some even resort to bank loans and spend several years paying for their surgeries and treatments, as may be observed in the following example, in which the woman reports that she is still paying for the surgery after eight years:

> la primera operación me ayudó mi mamá, yo era carga de ella en la:: isapre | pero salió terriblemente caro | y hasta el día de hoy estoy pagando: | pagándole | a mi mamá (My mom helped me for the first operation, the:: isapre [private health coverage] | but it was terribly expensive | and to this day I am paying: | paying | to my mom)

In order of frequency, the next entity that arose in the analysis was the health personnel. The appraisal was both positive and negative, and in many cases, they were discursively constructed in polar extremes, associated with war metaphors, portraying them as "heroes" or "enemies." Not only do medical doctors emerge in the corpus, but also nurses and mental health professionals. Regarding the preference for a male or female physicians, both were found in the corpus. When the patient evaluated her choice for a male gynecologist, she mentioned her values of intellectual reliability. When the professional was female, the reasons behind the preference mostly referred to solidarity, sympathy, and alignment, as can be seen in the following example:

me angustiaba el hecho de que muchas veces | cuando iba sobre todo a ginecólogos hombres como que me hacían sentir que yo estaba exagerando | como que no podía ser tanto el dolor | y como dentro de todo las ginecólogas en general sentía | no sé como que no me entendían | ... | y hasta que la ginecóloga con la que fui ese año | en realidad cuando me dijo como qué era lo que tenía (I was distressed by the fact that many times | when I went mostly to male gynecologists like they made me feel like I was exaggerating | like it couldn't be so much pain | and like in general with female gynecologists in general I felt | I don't know as if they didn't understand me | ... | and until the gynecologist I went with that year | actually it was then when she told me what I had)

Another frequent entity that emerged in the corpus comprises the patients' relatives, usually the mothers in the early stages of the condition. The category also included children, friends, colleagues, and partners. They are the subjects that usually constitute the affective networks of the patients, but their descriptions have a strong individual character. They focus on themselves and on what they have experienced, usually neglecting others around them. It is interesting that, contrary to our expectations, the entity "men" only appeared twice in the whole corpora. Another unexpected finding is the role assigned to motherhood. Our culturally impacted identities lead us to anticipate high percentages of references to fertility and the relevance of the pathology regarding the possibility of becoming mothers. However, the data showed the opposite. This can be observed in the following segment from an interview:

le conté [al médico] mi historia que quería operarme y me dijo::: no y yo como || ¿por qué? Me dijo no es que tú eres muy joven aún y yo ya:: ¿y qué? Me dijo no si te vai a operar hazlo cuando querai ser mamá y yo le dije es que:: yo no quiero ser mamá y me dijo ¡pero cómo si estai en una relación hace mucho tiempo! - porque en ese entonces llevaba cinco años pololeando … yo te aseguro que de aquí a cinco años tú vai a querer ser mamá y yo quedé como no en verdad no quiero jamás ha estado en mis planes la maternidad yo solo quiero mejorar mi calidad de vida | | me dijo no ¿y por qué no queris ser mamá? yo le dije pucha como que en verdad mis razones van en parte por conciencia medioambiental siento que el planeta no está para traer más gente al mundo | me dijo ¡aah! pero en ese caso te sucidai.

(I told [the doctor] my story that I wanted to have surgery and he told me::: no and I asked | | why? He told me no you're still very young and I said:: so what? He said no, if I operate on you and then you want to be a mother and I told him: I don't want to be a mother and he told me, but you've been in a relationship for a long time! - because at that time I had been going out for five years … I assure you that five years from now you will want to be a mother and I didn't really want to. I never wanted to. Motherhood has never been in my plans. I just want to improve my quality of life. | | He said no, and why don't you want to be a mom? I said to him, my reasons are partly due to environmental awareness, I feel that the planet is not in a condition to bring more people into the world | he told me oh! but in that case why don't you commit suicide?)

The example above is a clear illustration of how cultural factors have a direct impact on health practices. In this instance, the gynecologist refused to perform the surgical procedure and seriously questioned the patient's decision not to have children, regardless of her condition. Even when the topic was not relevant to this patient, the doctor emphasized the motherhood role that was culturally expected from a young woman.

When analyzing the corpus, it became evident that women who suffer from endometriosis worry most about pain and how it affects their quality of life. Facchin et al. (2015), in their article "Impact of endometriosis

on quality of life and mental health: Pelvic pain makes the difference,"
observed the significant impact of endometriosis on the patients' quality
of life, anxiety, and depression. They emphasize that the difference in life
quality really depends on whether the woman suffers pelvic pain. The
feeling is described as absolutely incapacitating. When patients are in deep
pain, nothing else matters to them. They cannot move; they cannot think;
all they want is to be free from pain. This, in turn, is associated with the idea
of a "normal life." In line with this notion of "normality," some even report
that they regret having normalized menstrual pain, and they all agree upon
the recurrent idea that female pain should not be considered normal.

The narratives, then, circle back to where they started. At first, they did
not know what was causing them debilitating pain, they had no information
about their condition, and because of that, they suffered terribly. Now they
know and feel responsible for making endometriosis visible to help other
women and for outweighing the cultural voice that imposes a model of
women who must endure suffering.

Concluding Remarks

It was 1979 when the International Association for the Study of Pain
(IASP) defined pain as "An unpleasant sensory and emotional experience
associated with actual or potential tissue damage, or described in terms of
such damage." It seems obvious nowadays to associate the phenomenon of
feeling pain with an emotional impact. It seems commonsensical to consider
that years of suffering a chronic disease like the one I have analyzed in my
study leave profound traces on a patient's personality and mental health.
Nevertheless, listening to the patients' voices is not as common of a practice
as it should be.

The objectives of this essay were to explore (1) how language is used
by Spanish-speaking women from Chile to construct meanings of affect

in narratives of endometriosis experiences across discourse genres, and (2) which entities these patients evaluate in their narratives. The implementation of analytical tools from the System of Appraisal have allowed us to identify patterns of evaluative meanings, in other words, evaluative prosodies that consolidate the idea that endometriosis patients usually suffer long years of chronic pain, not only physically but also emotionally. The normalization of female pain, the naturalization of menstrual suffering, and the cultural mistrust of women's emotions impoverish chronic patients' life quality. A lack of real concern prevents timely diagnosis and, in turn, the patients' possibilities of leading "normal" lives.

Our findings point to misconceptions, false expectations, imposed cultural roles, and a generalized lack of sympathy towards those who suffer. We hope to have contributed to a better understanding of what chronic pain patients feel, as well as what they care about and worry about. These results should raise our awareness of how sad they may feel and the need to play a more sensitive, compassionate role in social interaction. We also hope to have shed light on understanding how language operates in the construction of affective meanings, which may not be so clear to the untrained eye.

Acknowledgments

The author would like to thank the Fondecyt Grant 11190133 for financial support. She also thanks the many patients who participated in her studies.

Works Cited

Bañón Hernández, Antonio Miguel. 2018. *Discurso y Salud. Análisis de un Debate Social*. Primera. Navarra: Ediciones Universidad de Navarra (EUNSA).

Bonnin, Juan Eduardo. 2013. "The Public, the Private and the Intimate in Doctor-Patient Communication: Admission Interviews at an Outpatient Mental Health Care Service." *Discourse Studies* 15, no. 6: 687–711. https://doi.org/10.1177/1461445613492249.

Braghetto, Ítalo M., and Patricio Baronti. 2007. "Relación Paciente-Médico. Una Alianza Que Fomenta La Calidad* Relation Patient-Doctor and Quality of the Attention DOCUMENTOS." *Rev. Chilena de Cirugía* 59: 385–92.

Bukstein, Don A. 2016. "Patient Adherence and Effective Communication." *Annals of Allergy, Asthma & Immunology* 117, no. 6: 613–619. https://doi.org/10.1016/J.ANAI.2016.08.029.

Bullo, Stella. 2018. "Exploring Disempowerment in Women's Accounts of Endometriosis Experiences." *Discourse and Communication* 13, no. 6: 419–445. https://doi.org/10.1177/1750481318771430.

Bullo, Stella. 2019. "'I Feel like I'm Being Stabbed by a Thousand Tiny Men': The Challenges of Communicating Endometriosis Pain." *Health* (United Kingdom) 24, no. 5: 476–492. https://doi.org/10.1177/1363459318817943.

Bullo, Stella, and Jasmine Heath Hearn. 2020. "Parallel Worlds and Personified Pain: A Mixed-Methods Analysis of Pain Metaphor Use by Women with Endometriosis." *British Journal of Health Psychology* 26, no. 2: 271–288. https://doi.org/10.1111/bjhp.12472.

Charon, Rita, Sayantani DasGupta, Nellie Hermann, Craig Irvine, Eric Marcus, Edgar Rivera-Colon, Danielle Spencer, and Maura Spiegel. 2017. *The Principles and Practice of Narrative Medicine.* New York: Oxford University Press.

Creswell, John W., Vicki L. Plano-Clark, Michelle L. Gutmann, and William E. Hanson. 2003. "Advanced Mixed Methods Research Designs." In *Handbook of Mixed Methods in Social and Behavioral Research,* edited by Abbas Tashakkori, Charles Teddlie, and Charles B.

Teddlie, 209–40. Thousand Oaks, CA: Sage.

Dolan, Brian. 2015. "One Hundred Years of Medical Humanities: A Thematic Overview." In *Humanitas: Readings in the Development of the Medical Humanities*, edited by Brian Dolan, 1–30. University of California Medical Humanities Press.

Facchin, Federica, Giussy Barbara, Emanuela Saita, Paola Mosconi, Anna Roberto, Luigi Fedele, and Paolo Vercellini. 2015. "Impact of Endometriosis on Quality of Life and Mental Health: Pelvic Pain Makes the Difference." *Journal of Psychosomatic Obstetrics and Gynecology* 36, no. 4: 135–141. https://doi.org/10.3109/016748 2X.2015.1074173.

Fauconnier, Arnaud, Hocine Drioueche, Cyrille Huchon, Joseph du Cheyron, Emilie Indersie, Yasmine Candau, Pierre Panel, and Xavier Fritel. 2021. "Early Identification of Women with Endometriosis by Means of a Simple Patient-Completed Questionnaire Screening Tool: A Diagnostic Study." *Fertility and Sterility* 116, no. 6: 1580–1589. https://doi.org/10.1016/j.fertnstert.2021.07.1205.

Halliday, Michael A. K. 1978. *Language as Social Semiotic. The Discourse Studies Reader: Main Currents in Theory and Analysis*. London: Edward Arnold. https://doi.org/10.1075/z.184.53hal.

Halliday, Michael A. K. 2004. *An Introduction to Functional Grammar. An Introduction to Functional Grammar*, revised by Cristian M.I.M. Matthiessen. 3rd ed. London: Routledge. https://doi. org/10.4324/9780203783771.

Hållstam, Andrea, Britt-Marie Stålnacke, Christer Svensén, and Monika Löfgren. 2018. "Living with Painful Endometriosis – A Struggle for Coherence. A Qualitative Study." *Sexual & Reproductive Healthcare* 17 (October): 97–102. https://doi.org/10.1016/J.SRHC.2018.06.002.

Harvey, Kevin, and Nelya Koteyko. 2012. "Patients' Narratives of Health and Illness." In *Exploring Health Communication: Language in Action*, edited by Kevin Harvey and Nelya Koteyko, 70–92. London & New York: Routledge. https://doi.org/10.4324/9780203096437-11.

Hennegan, Julie, Inga T. Winkler, Chris Bobel, Danielle Keiser, Janie Hampton, Gerda Larsson, Venkatraman Chandra-Mouli, Marina Plesons, and Thérèse Mahon. 2021. "Menstrual Health: A Definition for Policy, Practice, and Research." *Sexual and Reproductive Health Matters* 29, no. 1: 31–38. https://doi.org/10.1080/26410397.2021.1911618.

Hudelist, Gernot, Nadya Fritzer, Almut Thomas, Christiane Niehues, Peter Oppelt, Dietmar Haas, Ayman Tammaa, and Heinrich Salzer. 2012. "Diagnostic Delay for Endometriosis in Austria and Germany: Causes and Possible Consequences." *Human Reproduction* 27, no. 12: 3412–3416. https://doi.org/10.1093/HUMREP/DES316

IASP. 1979. "Pain terms: a list with definitions and notes on usage: recommended by the IASP Subcommittee on Taxonomy." *Pain* 6, no. 3: 249.

Koller, Veronika, and Stella Bullo. 2019. "'Fight Like a Girl': Tattoos as Identity Constructions for Women Living with Illness." *Multimodal Communication* 8, no. 1: 20180006. https://doi.org/10.1515/mc-2018-0006.

Laganà, Antonio Simone, Valentina Lucia la Rosa, Agnese Maria Chiara Rapisarda, Gaetano Valenti, Fabrizio Sapia, Benito Chiofalo, Diego Rossetti, Helena Ban Frangež, Eda Vrtačnik Bokal, and Salvatore Giovanni Vitale. 2017. "Anxiety and Depression in Patients with Endometriosis: Impact and Management Challenges." *International Journal of Women's Health* 9: 323–330. https://doi.org/10.2147/IJWH.S119729.

Martin, James R. 1985. "Process and Text: Two Aspects of Human Semiosis." In *Systemic Perspectives on Discourse.*, edited by James Benson and William Greave, 1: 248–274. Norwood, NJ: Praeger.

Martin, James R. 2000. "Beyond Exchange: Appraisal Systems in

English." In *Evaluation in Text: Authorial Stance and the Construction of Discourse*, edited by Susan Hunston and Geoff Thompson, 142–175. Oxford: Oxford University Press.

Martin, James R. 2009. "Genre and Language Learning: A Social Semiotic Perspective." *Linguistics and Education* 20, no. 1: 10–21. https://doi.org/10.1016/j.linged.2009.01.003.

Martin, James R., and David Rose. 2007. *Working with Discourse: Meaning beyond the Clause*. London: Continuum.

Martin, James R., and Peter R.R. White. 2005. *The Language of Evaluation: Appraisal in English*. London: Palgrave Macmillan. https://doi.org/10.1057/9780230511910.

Ngo, Thu, and Len Unsworth. 2015. "Reworking the Appraisal Framework in ESL Research: Refining Attitude Resources." *Functional Linguistics* 2, no. 1: 1–24. https://doi.org/10.1186/s40554-015-0013-x.

Pascual, Mariana. 2020. "Discurso, Salud e Información desde el Relato de Pacientes de Endometriosis." *Discurso & Sociedad* 14, 2: 421–442. http://www.dissoc.org/ediciones/v14n02/DS14%282%29Pascual.pdf.

Pascual, Mariana. 2021. "Online Emotional Support: Discourse Functionalities on Chilean Facebook Pages by Patients with Chronic Pain." *Entrepalavras* 11, no. 3: 1–19. https://doi.org/10.22168/2237-6321-32298.

Pascual, Mariana, and Natalia Díaz Alegría. 2021. "El Afecto en Relatos de Dolor Crónico en Comentarios de Facebook de Mujeres Chilenas." *Nueva Revista Del Pacífico*, no. 74: 47–63. https://doi.org/10.4067/s0719-51762021000100047.

Rubinsky, Valerie, Jacqueline N. Gunning, and Angela Cooke-Jackson. 2018. "'I Thought I Was Dying:' (Un)Supportive Communication Surrounding Early Menstruation Experiences." *Health Communication*

35, no. 2: 242–52. https://doi.org/10.1080/10410236.2018.1548337.

Sánchez González, Miguel Ángel. 2017. "El Humanismo y la Enseñanza de las Humanidades Médicas." *Educación Médica* 18, no. 3: 212–218. https://doi.org/10.1016/j.edumed.2017.03.001.

Shahin, Wejdan, Gerard A. Kennedy, and Ieva Stupans. 2019. "The Impact of Personal and Cultural Beliefs on Medication Adherence of Patients with Chronic Illnesses: A Systematic Review." *Patient Preference and Adherence* 13: 1019–1035. https://doi.org/10.2147/PPA.S212046.

Stæhr, Andreas. 2015. "Reflexivity in Facebook Interaction - Enregisterment across Written and Spoken Language Practices." *Discourse, Context and Media* 8: 30–45. https://doi.org/10.1016/j.dcm.2015.05.004.

Teddlie, Charles, and Abbas Tashakkori. 2011. "Mixed Methods Research: Contemporary Issues in an Emerging Field." In *The SAGE Handbook of Qualitative Research*, edited by Norman K. Denzin and Yvonna S. Lincoln, 285–300. Thousand Oaks, CA: SAGE Publications, Inc.

Wodak, Ruth. 1997. "Critical Discourse Analysis and the Study of Doctor-Patient Interaction." In *The Construction of Professional Discourse*, edited by Britt-Louise Gunnarsson, Per Linell, and Bengt Nordberg, 173–200 London: Routledge.

4

Advance Health Care Directives, End-of-Life Considerations, and the COVID-19 Pandemic

Yu-Han Chao

Abstract:

With the uncertainty that the COVID-19 pandemic has brought into the lives of people across the world, Advance Health Care Directives and end-of-life considerations are no longer hypothetical thought exercises or unlikely legal what-ifs, but an important way to safeguard your and your loved ones' quality of life and wishes. The beginning of this paper discusses the author's own experience with end-of-life issues using her mother, who became critically ill and had no Advance Health Care Directive, as a case study. The paper then describes some of the author's experiences as an ICU nurse during the COVID-19 pandemic. Many patients' families had to make healthcare decisions for their family members without knowledge of their wishes and also with limited health literacy regarding disease processes, prognoses of their loved ones, and treatment options. The last section of the paper details parts of a typical Advance Health Care Directive Form. The general public often does not have a clear understanding of the process, risks, alternatives, and benefits of intubation, cardiopulmonary resuscitation, artificial nutrition, and other medical interventions. The author describes what these treatment options look like in reality, in addition to discussing quality of life and the patient experience.

Many cultures may traditionally consider it inauspicious to talk about end-of-life issues, but with the uncertainty that the COVID-19 pandemic has brought into the lives of people across the world, Advance Health Care Directives and end-of-life considerations are no longer hypothetical thought exercises or unlikely legal what-ifs, and are now an important way to safeguard our own and our loved ones' quality of life and wishes. There are many parts to an Advance Health Care Directive Form, and all of them are customizable to your preference. You can receive or decline the specific care and interventions desired should a medical need arise, designate a Power of Attorney (and back-up candidates) as a decision maker, and make clear whether you want certain interventions, such as chest compressions and electrical shocks to the heart, intubation to support breathing, artificial nutrition, or other measures.

This paper opens by discussing my experience with end-of-life issues with my mother as a case study. When my mother became ill in 2015, I was a college lecturer who had been in the humanities my entire life and possessed limited knowledge about medical terminology and interventions. My mother arrived by ambulance at a hospital in southern California, unconscious and septic. Not only had she practically never been to a doctor, she had no Advance Health Care Directive drawn up, and we had to guess her preferences in any given situation. At one point, many non-family members from the community tried to insert themselves into the decision-making process when we were discussing her code status and treatment options with the interdisciplinary healthcare team.

This paper highlights end-of-life concerns from my point of view as an Intensive Care Unit nurse during the COVID-19 pandemic. Many patients' families, much like my own when my mother became ill, had to make healthcare decisions for their ill family members without knowledge of their wishes and also with limited health literacy regarding disease processes, prognoses of their loved ones, and what treatment options really look like in reality. Because the novel coronavirus had the possibility of making many individuals with various risk factors critically ill, sometimes regardless of age, these patients' families not only experienced grief and fear, but were also faced with such impossible decisions that they had difficulty agreeing on a medical plan of care for their loved ones. Meanwhile, the patients remained intubated on breathing machines, suffered organ failure requiring daily dialysis, and required multiple intravenous medications around the clock, including sedation, analgesia, and sometimes paralytics, to help them remain compliant with mechanical ventilation and, ultimately, compatible with life.

Finally, various parts of a typical Advance Health Care Directive Form will be explained. This includes designating decision maker(s), instructions/wishes for health care, organ and tissue donation, and a primary care provider. The general public does not usually have a clear understanding of the process, risks, benefits, and alternatives of intubation, cardiopulmonary resuscitation, artificial nutrition, and other medical interventions. I will describe what some of these treatment options look like in reality, as well as discuss the importance of quality of life alongside the patient's experience and potential pain and suffering.

Case Study

My first introduction to Advance Health Care Directives and end-of-life issues was when my mother fell ill in the summer of 2015. That summer, bleary-eyed and sleep-deprived, with my three-year-old in tow while caring for my dying mother, I googled, "Do hospice patients live forever?"

I was not yet a Registered Nurse, but that summer, I was my mother's hospice nurse. Every two hours, I administered morphine sulfate, and every four to six hours, lorazepam, which, together with the morphine, helped manage her pain. Because she was dying. Her illness was sudden: bacterial meningitis, a result of the infected tumors in her uterus from endocervical cancer that had metastasized, or spread. She was always afraid of hospitals and never went to a doctor, even when she should have. She did not have a primary care physician even though she had many family friends who were doctors. No one knew she had cancer. Where she grew us, my brothers and me, death grew as well.

By the time my brothers and I were informed by my father about our mother's illness, and I traveled down to southern California from central California, she had already been transferred to a different, specialty hospital where she had her second surgery, a drill in her skull to insert a catheter to monitor and reduce elevated pressure in her brain. She was partially shaven, sedated, and intubated. Days passed, and the intensivist approached us to consent to another procedure, a laminectomy, to potentially restore her lower body motor function since she had displayed no reflexes below the waist after her initial hospital admission.

As an Intensive Care Unit nurse now, I look back and strongly question why they were suggesting invasive, costly surgery after surgery for someone filled with cancer, dying from bacterial meningitis, who had no quality of life or much life expectancy whatsoever. At the time, however, I knew little about medical topics, had to look up every other specialized term or acronym used by the healthcare team, and did not know what we were getting ourselves into. "If it would help Mom, of course, do it," we all thought, so she was subjected to a third procedure, which made no difference whatsoever in outcome. Nobody on the healthcare team mentioned hospice or comfort care until my aunt's pastor came in to visit and told my aunt that she should ask the doctor about hospice or palliative care. Pastors knew what near-death looked like, I guess. Hospice care is medical care that focuses on the palliation of a patient's pain and symptoms; hospice patients usually have a prognosis of six or fewer months to live. The goals of hospice care are prioritizing comfort and quality of life, as well as reducing pain and suffering (Ignatavicius and Workman 2013, 95). Comfort care, or palliative care, is healthcare that optimizes quality of life and comfort (the opposite of pain) in gravely ill patients.

Meanwhile, we visited my mother every day in the Critical Care Unit and waited, not knowing what else to do. I remember asking one of the nurses if the "Critical Care Unit" was the same as an Intensive Care Unit, and she said, "Yes," looking at me like I was stupid. I was too disappointed to feel offended because my limited understanding of medicine was this: ICU meant serious illness, and somehow if CCU were different from ICU, I could still hold onto the hope that my mother was not quite so sick. She was.

One day, when we were not present at the hospital, my mother's heart stopped, what we call a Code Blue in the ICU. As her code status was still the default "Full Code," the health care team did whatever it took to get her back, maybe compressions, maybe electrical shocks, maybe medications, or all of the above. Full code means that if someone's heart stops beating or they stop breathing, all resuscitation measures are provided to keep them alive. After they resuscitated and temporarily stabilized her, the doctor finally suggested that we consider changing her code status to DNR, do not resuscitate, so that if her heart stopped again, she could go in peace without being shocked or having her ribs fractured with compressions. A Taiwanese "family friend" who was not related to us, and whom my brothers and I did not know, had started asking the hospital for updates on his own after helping interpret what doctors were saying for my father before I arrived in southern California and became the new interpreter. An official interpreter trained in medical terminology or interpretation service really should have been used instead. This family friend found out what happened, that a DNR status was being recommended, and violated HIPAA (Health Insurance Portability and Accountability Act, regulations that protect patient privacy) by telling everybody in my mother's southern Californian, Taiwanese community about the matter.

Soon, my family and I received call after call from complete strangers (to us) that were friends of our mother's. With no understanding of her wishes, her prognosis, or the extreme measures already taken, these people pleaded with us to "give her another chance," to "please do not let her die, we love her so much," and so on. This made an already difficult decision and situation even harder, and certainly delayed the entire matter as well as the transition to comfort care for days because my aunt, swayed by the calls, became persuaded against the approach of comfort care. During this delay, my mother was kept at a level of sedation/anesthesia that would not have left her pain-free because she had to be checked for reflexes (which she was not displaying) and signs of improvement every shift, which is the common practice of intensive or critical care units.

As an ICU nurse now, I have learned that being intubated and ventilated by a breathing machine, as well as receiving the necessary care and treatment in a hospital, are not guaranteed to be pain- and discomfort-free, even with sedation and pain medication. I feel anger thinking back, knowing that my mother had been put through all those surgical procedures and futile interventions. It should have been quite clear, as soon as imaging showed she was full of cancer and testing revealed her blood and cerebral spinal fluids to be massively infected with bacteria, that there was no reason to keep her intubated for weeks while undergoing multiple invasive surgeries. The care she received was futile and, essentially, prolonged her suffering.

After many days of disagreements and delays, my family finally transitioned my mother to comfort care. After they unplugged her from the ventilator, we thought she would gasp for breath and crash, her organs shutting down one by one. Surprisingly, without the machine, she breathed quite well on her own, and my aunt began questioning the palliative care decision all over again, especially when she had to speak to more of our mother's friends, who had so wanted us to "Give her another chance." When my mother was considered stable a few hours after extubation (discontinuing intubation and ventilation), and once the hospital bed and oxygen tank had been delivered and set up at my parents' house, we went home to wait for her to arrive by ambulance. We would have her home with us, where the case manager and hospice nurses would train me to care for her, which I did until the case manager deemed her close enough to passing that hospice nurses were sent back to support us and pronounce her death.

The time between the beginning and the end of hospice stretched indefinitely. I felt delirious and numb from lack of sleep by day nineteen of, "I expect that she does not have a week," according to the palliative care doctor, whose bill for conversing with us for a few minutes was $1000. Staying alive was expensive. It turned out dying was as well. Two weeks in the ICU, three surgeries, followed by hospice. The bills started arriving. Arrangements had to be made. Funeral, burial, coffin, headstone.

Towards the end of her home hospice period, my mother was making a moaning kind of sound, as if in pain. In the beginning, we turned her every two hours, after her morphine. Now, the slightest touch brought on a grimace. Sometime during the last few nights, her soft, rattling moans became constant, with every breath. The night nurse said it was involuntary as it was rhythmic, and she was unlikely to be in pain. Just the normal, loosened vocal cords of a dying woman, vibrating. I did not know otherwise, and Google was no help. Another nurse came and went, also saying the sounds she was making were normal. All the nurses who visited or stayed said different things, however, I soon learned. Every time they told us to say our goodbyes, that today would be the day, or tonight would be the night, my mom hung on, like a zombie, and I woke up every hour at night, if I slept at all.

"Still zombie-ing," I updated my brothers on Google chat, and they knew I was talking about her, though I could just as well have been talking about myself.

Soon, she was moaning softly every second. My dad, who had given up sneak-feeding her his ginger concoction against the doctor's orders, still insisted on force-exercising her, as if his physical therapy would make her get up and walk again. As he moved her legs and arms in circles, she grimaced, and the nurse looked horrified.

"Stop it; you're abusing her," I barked at him.

He stopped, unhappy. None of us were happy. She was dying, and there was nothing we could do.

Nothing besides the morphine, lorazepam, and hyoscine tablets so she didn't choke to death on her own terminal fluids. It actually said "for terminal secretions" on the orange CVS bottle. The bottle looked exactly the same as any other prescription medication.

Nothing was ever what one expected.

All four of my grandparents were still alive, yet here was my mom, dying. We blamed it on American healthcare, or lack of it. She was afraid to go to the doctor, ever, because of the cost, and now she was dying, and racking up the medical bills anyway.

The morning nurse came.

"This isn't right," she said, when she heard the rhythmic moaning. "I don't like it."

She gave my mother an extra dose of morphine. She was too weak to even choke on it now; she slowly calmed down, and stopped moaning.

"Anything you want to say to her, tell her while you have a chance," the nurse said.

I trudged over to my mother's bedside, mumbled some vague thank-yous, and looked at her face.

It was white.

Now that I am a nurse, looking back, I question everything: the moaning, the multiple highly specialized surgeries for someone with poor prognosis and projected quality of life, why nobody talked to us about comfort care and hospice until we had to ask about it ourselves.

While having my mother in the ICU and on home hospice was a challenging time, I also cherished the time that I had with her. It was an honor and privilege to spend her final days with her, alleviate her pain with medications and soothe her with words, which we were told she could hear, because hearing is the last to go. Comfort care and hospice were also a much more peaceful process than one would expect, and it was wonderful to take my mother home to the house she had loved dearly, so she could live out her final days in the comfort of her own bedroom, where the sun shone in every morning, the breeze entered, and birds chirped outside the window all day long.

I hope as many people as possible can learn about Advance Health Care Directives and end-of-life concerns so that they can make their preferences for treatment known, ideally through official documentation, but even an informal (or formal) discussion with family members helps. That way, patients do not suffer needlessly or against their wishes, and their families do not experience the additionally complicated grief of having to make impossible healthcare decisions that may leave them with a lifetime of emotional turmoil, regret, guilt, trauma, and possibly, financial burden.

The COVID-19 Pandemic

When the first cases of coronavirus were being covered in the news, I was a Registered Nurse in the surgical department at our local hospital, where my clients were pre-and post-operative patients who had scheduled or emergent surgical procedures. Most day-shift surgical floor nurses had decades of experience, so without much seniority, I was the first to float to the COVID floors. This was early in the pandemic, when a nurse was Lysol-ed at a supermarket, healthcare workers were shunned like pariahs, and racist acts against Asian-Americans like myself were being reported in the news. I spent my birthday weekend alone at home because my ex-husband, who talked to me from behind a gate he would not open, refused to let me pick up my daughter per our custody agreement because I had been floated to the COVID floor. He did not want to put our daughter at risk, he said. The pandemic was bringing out the worst in all of us, it seemed. In the US, many individuals resisted masking, which protected others, because of their "right" not to wear a mask. I was afraid to go to the store, because of the above-mentioned Lysol incident, because I was Asian, and also because I did not want to catch COVID.

COVID patients who came in early on in their illness needed maybe two to fifteen liters of oxygen a minute delivered through flexible tubing, called nasal cannulas, to their nostrils. When patients did not improve because the virus had damaged the tiny air sacs called alveoli in their lungs, they often required a high-flow nasal cannula that delivered up to 60 liters of 100 percent, humidified oxygen a minute, or even a BiPAP (bilevel positive airway pressure) mask and machine. BiPAP machines pushed oxygen into the patients' lungs on inhalation and continued to force air in during exhalation to keep the air sacs in the lungs open and not collapsing. Many patients found the BiPAP masks highly uncomfortably and anxiety-inducing, yet if they took off their masks, within minutes their oxygen levels could fall to dangerously low levels. If patients were still struggling with BiPAP or high-flow nasal cannulas, with their oxygen levels continuing to decline, a provider usually ordered an ABG, arterial blood gas, to check the levels of carbon dioxide (waste) and oxygen (what we need to stay alive) in the blood. If the ABG level was not good, it would be time for the patient or their family to decide if intubation was something they desired, knowing that ventilation by machine also often meant sedative-hypnotics, possibly even paralytics, and no more talking. The prognosis of a COVID patient requiring mechanical ventilation was also extremely poor. By the time a patient required high levels of oxygen on high-flow nasal cannula and or a high percentage of oxygen on a BiPAP machine but still desaturated (experienced decreasing oxygen levels), they were often transferred to the ICU, due to the possibility of rapid decline and the potential need for intubation.

When elective surgeries were put on hold due to the pandemic (mostly scheduled knee or hip replacements), I began additional training and floated to the Intensive Care Unit, as there was a high demand for nurses to care for the increasing number of COVID patients on the unit.

I started in the ICU during the worst of the winter COVID surge of 2020. Just about every room had a COVID patient in it, and there were overflow ICU patients in the Post-Acute Recovery Unit, which used to be a fairly cheerful unit where surgical patients recovered briefly after a procedure, before going home or to another department or floor. Almost all the COVID patients were not only intubated, but also had an arterial line due to hemodynamic instability, and some also had multiple chest tubes to drain fluid and blood from their drowning lungs. Sometimes it seemed that if anyone so much as looked at a patient, their oxygen level desaturated to unacceptable levels that may require strenuous manual bagging with a bag valve mask that pumped air into the patient's airway, the sanitary in-hospital equivalent of forceful mouth-to-mouth resuscitation.

There have been patients who were able to be weaned off a ventilator and sedation and woke up after having been intubated for months. One reported that the routine suctioning that we performed on ventilated patients as frequently as needed and at least every three or four hours felt like their "brains were being sucked out." Repositioning or proning (being turned onto the belly, a practice that helped some patients' lungs) could feel like they were "being dropped on the floor." Hallucinations were also possible side effects of some medications necessary to support patients' lives and intended to keep them comfortable. Some patients who survive but cannot get off the breathing machine get a tracheostomy, an incision in the throat to insert a breathing tube, which is then connected to a mechanical ventilator so that they can continue to receive breathing support. Once these "trached" patients are deemed stable enough to no longer have to be in a regular intensive care unit, they can transition to long-term acute care hospitals. Usually, the tracheostomy and PEG (percutaneous endoscopic gastrostomy, a feeding tube surgically inserted into the stomach through the abdominal and stomach walls) insertion procedures are done at the same time so that the patient can be maintained long-term on oxygen and nutrition. Those were our success stories, the patients who were transferred out of the hospital alive after months of intubation after COVID had ravaged their bodies.

Families cried over their hospitalized family member on one end of their devices at home while we held up an iPad in the negative pressure COVID room so that the family could see their ill loved one, and family conferences were held over the phone while the doctors discussed next steps and treatment options. Sometimes the process felt like grasping at straws because most of these patients, once they required a breathing machine, would not make it, and their families had great difficulty grasping that, so the healthcare team tried more medications, ventilator settings, more interventions. The families came armed with prayers from entire congregations, buoyed by stories of someone who was related to someone they knew who had woken up just fine from a five-year coma, but the thing was that those stories were not about COVID patients. COVID was new, different, capable of causing damage to every body system or organ, and terrifying. We fought it, and the patients and their families fought it valiantly as well, until the very end.

Nobody seemed safe until finally, new mRNA (messenger ribonucleic acid) vaccines entered the scene. Healthcare workers got vaccinated, the elderly and immunocompromised got vaccinated, the general public got vaccinated, and now, finally, children can get vaccinated against COVID-19 as well. The elderly could finally safely gather with their family members again. The socially isolated children (and their longsuffering, homeschooling parents) had endured enough.

Over time, from what we were seeing in the hospital, vaccination, whether Johnson & Johnson, Pfizer or Moderna, often made the difference between a) a COVID-positive grandma chilling on room air or b) an unvaccinated, previously healthy young father kept alive (barely) by a ventilator pushing 100 percent oxygen hard and fast into his scrub-daddy lungs, whose cardiovascular system needed continuous IV medication to halfheartedly pump blood and whose kidneys filtered nothing and necessitated daily dialysis. Additionally, the pain and discomfort of his illness and such necessary interventions required continuous opioid pain medication and sedative-hypnotics or he would not be able to bear another minute of it all. A tracheostomy, PEG tube and living out the remainder of life in a long-term acute care hospital would be the happy ending here— only it wasn't, really.

Working in a COVID ICU was challenging, especially when it came to seeing hopeful or grieving families on the other end of the iPad, seeing pictures of our patients' babies, or even witnessing their elderly family members crying outside their rooms, collapsing into wheelchairs after they passed.

It has truly been an honor, however, to be able to take care of patients in their final days, final hours, to be one of the last people to clean them, care for them, talk to them, or hold up an iPad so their family can say goodbye and express their love for them. I am grateful every day for my job and feel privileged to be there, too often at the end.

Advance Health Care Directive Forms

The California Advance Health Care Directive Form that I use as a reference is just a sample of a generic Advance Health Care Directive Form – every part of it is customizable to the user's preference – no standard format is required. It does allow you to specify which individual(s) can serve as your decision maker(s) if you become incapacitated, provides examples of what types of care may be offered in the event of a medical emergency, and allows you to state your preferences should similar situations arise. While competent and able to make your own decisions, you can also revoke or replace an Advance Health Care Directive Form at any point.

Part 1. Power of Attorney for Health Care
Part 1 allows you to designate another individual as an agent to make health care decisions for you. You may state whether the medical decision maker can start making decisions for you upon the signing of the Advance Directive form, or only if and when you become incapable of making your own healthcare decisions. You can limit the authority of an agent as much or as little as desired. An agent may consent to any care, imaging, tests, surgical procedures, and medications not specifically excluded in the Advance Health Care Directive.

Withholding or providing artificial nutrition and hydration are also decisions to be made. Artificial nutrition and hydration come with risks depending on the method—intravenous (IV) nutrition carries the risk of infection, and artificial nutrition/formula using a feeding tube that goes through the nostril, down the esophagus, and into the stomach can be exactly as uncomfortable as it sounds. A surgically-inserted tube into the stomach for nutrition requires an invasive procedure that also comes with typical surgery-related risks, including infection and bleeding. Since nutrition and hydration may also prolong life expectancy unless severe complications occur, quality of life should be considered, too—a longer life spent in pain, especially if you remain under "full code" status that allows for repeated vigorous compressions of the chest (which can fracture ribs), electrical shocks, and other heroic measures to bring you back even if you stop breathing or your heart stops.

Part 2. Instructions for Health Care

In Part 2, you can delineate your wishes regarding treatment to keep you alive, requested pain relief, and other additional wishes. It can be as general or specific as you desire.

Regarding end-of-life decisions, you can tick the box in front of "choice not to prolong life" or "choice to prolong life." Choosing not to prolong life indicates, "I do not want my life to be prolonged if (1) I have an incurable and irreversible condition that will result in my death within a relatively short time, (2) I become unconscious and, to a reasonable degree of medical certainty, I will not regain consciousness, or (3) the likely risks and burdens of treatment would outweigh expected benefits" (Advance Health Care Directive Form). The choice to prolong life option means, "I want my life to be prolonged as long as possible within the limits of generally accepted health care standards" (Advance Health Care Directive Form). These descriptions are broad enough that it still takes medical professionals a reasonable amount of time and diagnostic tests or imaging to determine whether a condition is "incurable and irreversible" or whether one may "regain consciousness." Some people have the misconception that choosing not to prolong life means if someone goes to the hospital nobody will do anything. The healthcare team does everything except what Advance Health Care Directives specifically instruct them not to do.

The pain-relief section form outlines, "Except as I state in the following space, I direct that treatment for alleviation of pain or discomfort to be provided at all times, even if it hastens my death: [space provided]"

(Advance Health Care Directive Form). Sometimes pain can be so great that the amount of medication needed to alleviate it may reduce the patient's ability to breathe, affect their level of consciousness, and can hasten death.

Other wishes can be anything else you feel strongly concerned about, from ventilators and dialysis to feeding tubes or blood transfusions. One of my specific wishes, personally, is never to be intubated, because of the poor prognosis of someone requiring a ventilator to stay alive as well as the discomfort involved in the process of intubation and staying on a ventilator. This would not happen if I were not intubated, but I definitely do not want to get a tracheostomy, a surgical incision made in the throat and trachea to allow someone to live long-term on a breathing machine, either. Neither do I want artificial nutrition provided through a PEG tube. "Trach and PEG" are common goals for patients who have been intubated for a prolonged time in the ICU, and they are as invasive as they sound. I want none of that, even if it "saves" my life, because I do not want to live with a tracheostomy in my throat and a PEG tube in my stomach, dependent on machines and healthcare professionals to keep me alive. I have a right to choose not to live a certain way—we all do.

Individual medications or treatments can require an explanation of risks, alternatives, and benefits from the provider to the decision maker in order for informed consent to be given. Sometimes societal stigma and misconceptions around opioid pain medications cause the general public to fear medications like morphine and fentanyl, whether it is due to negative media coverage or fears that their loved ones may become addicted to the medication. Using opioid pain medication to alleviate pain and suffering in the intensive care unit or at the end of life is nothing like people self-injecting or ingesting illegal street drugs to chase a high. The eighty-five-year-old who needed morphine to tolerate the pain of a massive abdominal surgery is not going to head onto the streets looking for another hit of morphine after recovering from surgery and going home. It may be useful to indicate in the Advance Health Care Directive document that one is receptive towards opioids or other pain medications or sedatives as necessary to reduce pain and suffering, or state otherwise.

If there are any preferences regarding having a spiritual leader visit at end of life, whether one prefers to die at home or at a healthcare facility, whether one wants an autopsy, and whether one desires to be buried or cremated, that can be documented as well.

Part 3. Donation of Organs, Tissues, and Body Parts at Death
Part 3 of the Advance Health Care Directive Form shares your wishes regarding whether to donate organs, tissues, and body parts after brain death. The American Academy of Neurology guidelines determine brain death through four prerequisites that must all be met. The four criteria are the following: coma of known cause, normal or near-normal body temperature, systolic blood pressure greater than 100mmHg, and at least one neurologic examination, usually by a neurologist or intensive care physician (Ignatavicius and Workman 2013, 954). These strict prerequisites for defining brain death may help alleviate the general public's misconceptions and concerns around organ donation, such as the (misguided) fear that their organs may be harvested from them while they are "still alive" if they sign up to be an organ donor. Brain death is essentially death, especially when the rest of the body is maintained temporarily by a breathing machine, artificial nutrition, and other modern medical interventions. Brain death may be diagnosed through tests such as cerebral angiography, electroencephalography, and cerebral computed tomographic angiography (Ignatavicius and Workman 2013, 954). The Uniform Determination of Death Act states: "An individual who has sustained either (1) irreversible cessation of circulatory and respiratory functions, or (2) irreversible cessation of all functions of the entire brain, including the brain stem, is dead. A determination of death must be made in accordance with accepted

medical standards" (Determination of Death 2015).

One can indicate whether, after a diagnosis of brain death, one wants to contribute body parts for transplant, therapy, research, or education (such as for teaching residents at a teaching hospital). According to the Health Resources and Services Administration, as of March 2022, there are 106,242 people on the national transplant waiting list in the US, seventeen people die each day while waiting for an organ, and one person's donation of organs can save as many as eight lives (Organ Donation Statistics). Every nine minutes, another person is added to the organ donation waiting list in the US, and the donation of other parts can enhance the lives of seventy-five others who may not have life-threatening conditions but who can benefit from cornea, skin, or other donations (Organ Donation Statistics). A patient and their family may find great comfort in knowing that they were able to save the lives of as many as eight people and greatly improve the quality of lives of many more.

Part 4. Primary Physician

In Part 4, one can designate a physician to have primary responsibility for one's health care, if desired. Since trust and communication are important when discussing end-of-life care, selecting a physician one knows and trusts may be helpful to the process, if at all possible, depending on insurance coverage and availability.

Part 5-7. Signature and Witnesses

Finally, like any legal document, a signature concludes and confirms the content of the form. Once the Advance Health Care Directives Form is completed, one can take it to a notary public to be notarized, or alternatively, have two witnesses sign the form instead of hiring a notary public. The only requirements for the witnesses are that they may not be the patient's family members or a beneficiary of the patient's estate, nor can they be the patient's health care providers or workers at a health care facility where the patient currently resides.

Conclusion

In many cultures and communities across the world, people may shy away from talking about death and dying due to taboos and such topics being considered morbid or unlucky. Yet, after experiencing an unprecedented pandemic in recent human history, we are reminded daily of the fragility of life and the inevitability of death. In the face of such vicissitudes of life, discussing hypothetical treatment preferences and end-of-life care with family and having a completed Advance Health Care Directive is not only wise, it prevents unnecessary (additional) pain, suffering, and turmoil, and is also a responsible and prudent practice. Advance Health Care Directives should be treated as required, with matter-of-fact paperwork to be completed in the same way people set up trusts, list beneficiaries for their retirement accounts and investments, and write out their wills.

Usually, in acute care, we take all the heroic measures available to us to help patients fight for their lives and to support all their organs and functions, unless otherwise specified in their code status. Code status may be Do Not Resuscitate, Do Not Intubate, or otherwise-specified Limited Code that states exactly what the patient or family wishes to have done or not done. The healthcare team always follows patients' wishes as stated in their documents or as shared by their decision makers. Without clear Advance Health Care Directives, it is important to consider quality of life and whether the patient may be suffering with little to no hope of leaving the hospital. Comfort care and hospice can be very peaceful, dignified, gentle, and ultimately, kind, as it was for my mother and for many of our patients. In particular, during the COVID pandemic, there was nothing worse than going through code blue after code blue on the same patient until, eventually, nothing would bring them back, when the endless compressions, manual ventilation, shocks, medications, all of our "heroic" measures stopped working. Drenched in sweat in our plastic gowns, shields, N-95s, and other PPE, we finally give up, staring at the flat line on the electrocardiogram while the vitals monitor beeps urgently, objecting to the lethal heart rhythm that the program knows is incompatible with life.

Advance Health Care Directives make sure patients receive exactly the care they would have wanted, are not shocked, cardioverted, ventilated, or operated on against their will, and receive all the treatments that they do want. In the face of a pandemic, more than ever before, it is important for people to address the different parts of the Advance Health Care Directives form as desired: designating decision-maker(s), instructions/wishes for health care, organ and tissue donation, and primary care provider. Healthcare workers want the best quality of life possible for their patients, and if death should come, the less pain and more peace and dignity, the better, but most of all, it is paramount to honor the wishes of patients and their decision makers, which can be clearly stated and documented in an Advance Health Care Directive Form.

I miss my mother and cherish every moment I had with her, from going to nightmarkets in Taiwan with her as a child to caring for her in her last days in America. I also wish we had not put her through the pain of three futile surgeries, two weeks of intubation in the ICU, and forced resuscitation (maybe compressions, maybe electrical shocks) when she coded. We had to make impossible decisions on her behalf, and I question them to this day.

Works Cited

"Advance Health Care Directive Form," State of California Department of Justice. Accessed January 2019. https://oag.ca.gov/sites/all/files/agweb/pdfs/consumers/ProbateCodeAdvancedHealthCareDirective Form-fillable.pdf.

"Determination of Death," Uniform Determination of Death Act § 1 (2015).

HRSA organdonor.gov "Organ Donation Statistics," Health Resources and Services Administration. Accessed March 2022. https://www.organdonor.gov/learn/organ-donation-statistics.

Ignatavicius, Donna D., and M. Linda Workman. 2013. *Medical-Surgical Nursing: Patient-Centered Collaborative Care*. 8th ed. St Louis, Missouri: Elsevier Saunders.

5

Successful Global Health Partnerships Between Kansas and Congo: Addressing Capacity Building Needs, Ebola, and COVID-19

Ithar Hassaballa and Ruaa Hassaballa-Muhammad

Abstract:

Community engagement and participation are critical in addressing public health concerns, particularly contagious disease outbreaks that impact health, psychosocial, sociocultural, and environmental factors. Still, a top-down approach to public health often misses opportunities for innovation and authentic engagement. This essay describes key lessons learned from the Ebola response effort (2014-2016) and the COVID-19 response effort (2019-2020) over the course of a partnership between the World Health Organization's (WHO) Regional Office for Africa and the WHO's Collaborating Centre (WHO CC) for Community Health and Development at the University of Kansas. They worked together to create Africa-related examples for the Community Tool Box, evaluate the Ebola response effort through the Community Check Box, create an African Health Action Toolkit, publish collaborative manuscripts on the Ebola response effort, and evaluate the COVID-19 response effort across the African region.

Collaborative, community-engaged, comparative work is crucial in addressing gaps related to public health and development. This chapter describes such work between the World Health Organization's (WHO) Regional Office for Africa and the WHO's Collaborating Centre (WHO CC) for Community Health and Development at the University of Kansas from 2011 to 2022. The two organizations worked together to: 1) create Africa-related examples for the Community Tool Box, an online resource for building healthy communities through capacity-building; 2) evaluate the Ebola response effort and address a needed evaluation gap using the Community Check Box monitoring and evaluation tool; 3) create an online African Health Action Toolkit to address public health goals; 4) Publish collaborative manuscripts on the Ebola response effort, and 5) evaluate the COVID-19 response effort across the African region (in 47 of 54 countries). Collaborative community engagement is critical in addressing public health concerns, particularly with contagious disease outbreaks that impact health, psychosocial, sociocultural, and environmental factors. Comparative work further allows lessons learned from past disease outbreaks to be applied when new outbreaks happen and for communities to learn from one another globally in responding to public health issues. Engaging African communities in addressing their own community needs and concerns is not a new concept, as can be seen from community-based participatory research. Still, a top-down approach to public health often misses opportunities for innovation and authentic engagement. This effort produced abundant opportunities for engaging various team members, including the authors (who contributed to these projects). This chapter highlights the strengths and barriers of this partnership; we share our own lessons learned as team members on these projects, which could benefit others doing similar work related to global health engagements.

The collaboration between the University of Kansas's Center for Community Health and Development and the WHO's Regional Office for

Africa encompassed capacity-building, technical support, and participatory evaluation efforts at the global level to address Ebola and COVID-19. Two approaches that have prompted collaborative work and translated public health knowledge into practice are capacity building and participatory evaluation (Fawcett et al. 2003; Chinman et al. 2005). Technical support included training and using internet-based tools such as the "Community Tool Box," which have also catalyzed the translation of knowledge into practice (Fawcett, Francisco, and Schultz 2004). These efforts have resulted in several collaborative products that have the potential to influence health throughout the African region. Working over time and across contexts, this chapter shows the dynamic nature of public health work: as new opportunities and challenges emerged, both organizations adapted to address timely concerns.

The Collaborating Organizations

The World Health Organization was established on April 7, 1948 to direct and coordinate authority on international health within the United Nation's system by 1) providing leadership, 2) shaping the research agenda, 3) setting norms and standards, 4) articulating evidence-based policies, 5) providing technical support and sustainable capacity, and 6) monitoring health trends (WHO 2016). Comprised of 7,000 workers in 150 country offices within six global regions, the WHO is headquartered in Geneva, Switzerland. WHO's collaborators include the United Nations, non-State actors, WHO Collaborating Centers, and Advisory Committees.

The WHO's Regional Office for Africa (WHO AFRO) is based in Brazzaville, Congo. WHO AFRO includes forty-seven of the fifty-four African countries, with seventeen countries from West Africa, ten from Central Africa, and twenty from East and South Africa. Established in 1952 and led by the Regional Director Dr. Matshidiso Rebecca Moeti, WHO

AFRO enables people in Africa "to attain the highest level of health" (WHO AFRO 2014). Another function of WHO AFRO is to gather, analyze, and disseminate information on different health concerns. At the regional level, there were five priority areas at the time, one of which was communicable diseases and the other of which was preparedness, surveillance, and response.

The WHO AFRO Health Promotion Cluster is tasked with promoting health, preventing non-communicable diseases, addressing social determinants of health, and improving urban health. This cluster focuses on health promotion at all stages of life through creating healthy environments (e.g., physical/built, social, economic, food/nutrition, etc.), addressing socio-economic factors related to health, and ultimately bridging the health equity gap (WHO AFRO 2014).

There are inequities among countries, counties, districts, and villages in Africa that contribute to a high incidence of disease, disability, and premature death. For example, politically stable countries like Tanzania have a higher quality of life than those countries with political instability. These inequities propel WHO to enhance the social and economic factors that determine people's opportunities for health. Multi-sectoral action is needed to coordinate these efforts as well as to address poverty and income inequality effectively. The environment plays a major role in community members' health, for example. Unsafe drinking water and poor sanitation and hygiene directly affect people's health and increase the rate of infectious diseases such as cholera and polio. These sectors include but are not limited to housing, water, food, security, sanitation, policy, finance and economic development, and transportation. Although the health sector is key in ensuring a high quality of life, structural determinants (e.g., policies) play a significant role in public health. WHO AFRO takes a holistic view of the factors that determine health both directly and indirectly and identifies the best approaches to address these issues depending on the context. Each

WHO AFRO country or member state is culturally, politically, economically, and linguistically unique, thus requiring unique action plans and strategies to address health issues. One of the key challenges is that even within each member state, each region, town, or village can have a diverse set of people with different cultural beliefs, languages, and community challenges. Compared to other countries around the globe, African countries are generally the most culturally and linguistically diverse. For example, Togo is home to 37 ethnic groups who speak 39 different languages (Morin, 2013).

WHO's Collaborating Center at the University of Kansas

The Center for Community Health and Development (CCHD), a WHO Collaborating Centre, is located at the University of Kansas and is affiliated with the Department of Applied Behavioral Science and the Schiefelbusch Institute for Life Span Studies. The CCHD's mission is to support community health and development through collaborative research and evaluation, teaching, training, technical assistance, and capacity building. Established in 1975, the CCHD uses behavioral instruction to help prepare people to take action and bring about community change (Fawcett et al 2000). The CCHD's efforts have been influenced by multiple disciplines, including behavioral psychology, public health, community psychology, and anthropology, to name a few. In 1990, the CCHD began providing evaluation and technical support for multiple foundation-funded initiatives, such as Project Freedom, the School Community Sexual Risk Reduction Project, and Neighborhood and Community Improvement Projects. At the same time, the CCHD was developing methods for reliably measuring community/system change as an intermediate outcome that can affect the environment, behavior, and health-related outcomes. The Center for Disease Control and Prevention recognized this community measurement approach as a model for assessing community change (for an example on an initiative evaluating cardiovascular disease, see Fawcett et al. 1998).

In 1995, the CCHD developed the Community Toolbox (CTB). The CTB is a tool that offers communities step-by-step processes on how to build healthy communities. The CTB also offers a space for communities to share how they have used the tools to solve public and community health and development problems. In 1996, the CCHD developed the online monitoring and evaluation (M&E) system, now named the Community Check Box, to continue participatory evaluation services. Designated as a WHO Collaborating Center on October 15, 2004, the CCHD uses its capabilities to support WHO Regional offices, particularly in Africa, the Americas, and the Middle East. WHO Collaborating Centres are university or academic institutions designated by the Director-General to carry out activities that support WHO programs.

The KU WHO CC's focus on capacity-building can be understood as the advancement of knowledge and skills among practitioners; the expansion of support and infrastructure for health promotion in organizations; and the development of cohesiveness and partnerships for health in communities (Fawcett 2008), as laid out by Smith, Tang, and Nutbeam, 2006. At the organizational level, this includes training staff on how to develop policies and procedures as well as how to plan, implement, and evaluate efforts. At the community level, capacity-building is related to the community's ability to take action to address their needs through increased awareness and access to resources. Capacity-building at both levels is important to assure effective mobilization, assessment, planning, action, evaluation, and sustainability. The WHO CC at KU's focus on technical assistance ensures that there is the training and support needed to implement key processes and sustain collaborative projects, such as training related to community engagement, evaluation, or action planning (Fawcett et al. 2000). Technical assistance is usually provided by an outside partner with specific expertise, such as an academic institution, and can be delivered in person or through the Internet (Chinman et al. 2005).

The Community Tool Box

The WHO CC at KU developed the Community Tool Box (CTB) in 1995 —an internet-based resource for building capacity. More than twenty years later, the CTB has over 300 educational modules and 8,000 pages of how-to guidance with sixteen Toolkits, each addressing a core competency in building healthy communities. The sixteen CTB Toolkits are:

1. Creating and Maintaining Partnerships
2. Assessing Community Needs and Resources
3. Analyzing Problems and Goals
4. Developing a Framework or Model of Change
5. Developing Strategic and Action Plans
6. Building Leadership
7. Developing an Intervention
8. Increasing Participation and Membership
9. Enhancing Cultural Competence
10. Advocating for Change
11. Influencing Policy Development
12. Evaluating the Initiative
13. Implementing Social Marketing
14. Writing a Grant Application for Funding
15. Improving Organizational Management and Development
16. Sustaining the Work or Initiative

The sixteen core competencies emerged from the capacity-building framework, which includes understanding community context, collaborative planning, developing leadership and enhancing participation, community action and intervention, evaluation, and promoting and sustaining the initiative (Fawcett et al. 2000). The CTB's content is readable, printable, and downloadable, including facilitators' guides and PowerPoint presentations. In their 2008 article, Fawcett and colleagues noted some current uses of the CTB: 1) instantly available resource for capacity-builders worldwide, 2) training, 3) technical assistance, 4) university instruction, 5) certification, and 6) building capacity for funded initiatives (Fawcett et al. 2008). Another feature of the CTB is its accessibility. The search tab allows for finding information efficiently. Additionally, the Troubleshooting Guide makes it easier for communities to access tools in order to address a current problem (i.e., there is opposition to a public health effort). The "Ask an Advisor" feature allows public health practitioners to ask advisors specific questions related to planning, implementation, or evaluation of their efforts. Finally, the Guest Book feature allows users to comment on what worked or did not work, questions they have, or recommendations for improvement.

The Community Tool Box (CTB) is the largest online resource for those working to build healthy communities. The CTB is currently available in English, Spanish, Arabic, and Farsi; with millions of user sessions annually, it has reached those working in over 230 countries around the world (CTB, 2022). Users of the CTB include community members, organizations, public health professionals, educational institutions, and students. Because it is a free, open-access resource, the CTB attracted six million users in 2016. WHO CC staff train organizations on essential elements of achieving success such as assessment, strategic planning, and evaluation.

Qualitative data from the CTB Guest Book, email, and personal communications suggest that the Africa-based CTB examples are being used by various groups, including community members, public health practitioners, and educational institutions, to build healthy communities. Community members use the CTB to assess community concerns and take action to address issues. The CTB examples of how others addressed concerns (e.g., communities in Kenya addressing sanitation concerns) have helped provide information on how others in similar contexts can achieve success. These tools empower people to address community problems with available resources.

Public health practitioners systematically use the CTB Toolkits and their examples to assess, plan, act, evaluate, and sustain efforts. This has been done since 2013, when WHO AFRO adopted the CTB as one of its core strategies for health promotion from 2013 to 2017 (WHO AFRO, 2013). Additionally, WHO AFRO and country partners in Guinea used the CTB Troubleshooting Guide to address opposition during the Ebola outbreak: community members attacked community health workers because they opposed health promotion activities. Community members blamed national leadership for the Ebola outbreak. Using the Troubleshooting Guide, WHO AFRO engaged local leaders in developing a plan to combat community resistance and opposition.

Educational institutions in Africa have also been using the CTB examples to address community health and development concerns, including both teachers and students in the process. A particular case is the University for Development Studies (UDS), located in Tamale, Ghana. This university created a master's in science program in Community Health and Development based on the CTB curriculum. Lecturers at UDS teach students how to assess, plan, and evaluate a community problem. Students are then sent to villages in the North Ghana region to assess community needs and plan an intervention to address communities' concerns collaboratively. Students are in the field for three weeks to complete the assessment and planning phases, then return to the classroom to refine their plans, learn how to intervene, and sustain the effort. They return to the field for six weeks to complete the implementation phase and plan for sustainability. Using a participatory process, students collaborate with the village chief, the elders, and community members.

The Community Check Box: A Monitoring and Evaluation System

WHO CC at KU's staff have been evaluating population-level projects for more than twenty years at the local, national, and global levels. The participatory evaluation has been used to understand: 1) the implemented intervention components; 2) the intervention components that produced change at the community and systems levels; 3) changes in population-level behaviors; and 4) changes in the outcome of interest.

Participatory evaluation research is a process by which local people and organizations collaborate with scientific partners (evaluation consultants) in setting the research agenda, gathering information, making sense of it, and using the information to calibrate and adjust (Leung, Yen, and Minkler 2004). Local people's participation provides access to local knowledge and expertise, ensuring that the research questions and methods fit their needs and are culturally responsive (Fawcett et al. 2008). According to Cousins and Whitmore (1998), participatory evaluation can be practical or transformative. Practical evaluation focuses on decision-making and problem solving, while transformative evaluation focuses on social justice and empowering those who have historically been excluded. Both practical and transformative evaluations are needed to solve global health problems and ensure inclusion of those most affected by health issues resulting in health inequities.

In 2003, Dr. Fawcett, from the KU WHO CC, and colleagues developed a Participatory Evaluation Framework (see Figure 1) that has been used to evaluate projects related to infant mortality, diabetes, obesity, violence, drug use, and several other significant population-level concerns. This conceptual framework has been used to guide evaluation efforts through the engagement of stakeholders to 1) name and frame the problem or goal; 2) develop a logic model to achieve success; 3) identify research questions and methods; 4) document the intervention; 5) make sense of the data; and 6) use the information to celebrate successes and make adjustments (Fawcett et al. 2003). To facilitate participatory evaluation, an online M&E system was developed by the WHO CC (Fawcett et al. 2008) that later came to be called the Community Check Box. The M&E system is used to: a) Capture (document) activities related to program implementation; b) code these events using an established scheme (e.g., Services Provided, Community/ System Changes, Development Activity, Dissemination Efforts, or

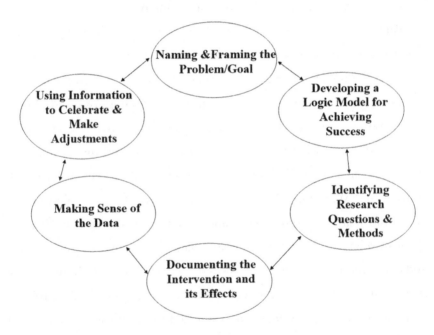

Figure 1: Participatory Evaluation Framework

[Note. This model is used to guide the participatory evaluation initiatives by the Center for Community Health and Development (Fawcett et al. 2003).]

Resources Generated); c) characterize the attributes of each activity (e.g., by goal addressed, strategy used, intervention component, etc.); and d) communicate findings through graphs of project implementation.

In addition to historical (e.g., slavery, colonialism) and structural (e.g., exclusion) factors, a particular challenge in the African region is that global health and development agencies have few resources to train a diverse and distributed workforce through capacity building (WHO AFRO 2013). Resource limitations are partially caused by the inability of agencies, particularly the WHO, to allocate resources to develop Africa-centered contextually appropriate tools or to receive training from those who understand the cultural and contextual background, especially those of African descent. A related problem is the lack of culturally sensitive tools and resources available to address the social determinants of health in the African region (Personal Communication 2014). Tools and frameworks from high-income countries with different economic, political, social, and public health infrastructures make health promotion projects impossible to implement in the African region due to lack of adaptability. It is important to ensure that the public health workforce has the tools and skills needed to address pressing concerns, hence the prioritization of these collaborations between KU's WHO CC and WHO AFRO on tools such as the Community Tool Box and Community Check Box. WHO partners in the African region were able to translate resources to local languages and develop tools that were culturally adaptive to the environment. Our continuing collaborations later resulted in the Action Toolkit and allowed us to be prepared to work together on COVID-19 response throughout Africa —we explain the evolution of our collaborative relationship and those later approaches below.

Collaborations Between WHO AFRO and WHO CC: Building Authentic Relationships and Trust for Over a Decade

In 2009, Dr. Stephen Fawcett, of KU's WHO CC, attended the 7th Global Conference on Health Promotion in Nairobi, Kenya, where he and Dr. Davison Munodawafa worked on a global strategy for addressing health and wellbeing for all people, resulting in a paper on community empowerment (Fawcett et al. 2010). During the same meeting, Dr. Fawcett introduced Dr. Munodawafa to the Community Tool Box (CTB). WHO AFRO colleagues saw an opportunity for the WHO CC to address some of their needs using the CTB. Colleagues in Africa found the CTB useful, but at the same time identified a gap: few examples were relevant to the African context. To address this disparity, the WHO CC offered Kansas Health Foundation Fellowships to undergraduate students with experience in Africa or African studies to develop and disseminate examples of building healthy communities using Africa-specific health issues and African-based talent and strategies for addressing these problems. The adaptation of the CTB examples to fit the African context occurred largely between 2011 and 2013.

A three-member Africa team comprised of students from Ghana (Sarafina Kankam), Kenya (Anne Nzuki), and Sudan (Ithar Hassaballa) developed and disseminated Africa-specific case examples for the CTB by highlighting the work of various organizations to address issues of most concern in the region. The purpose of the adaptation was to ensure context-specific information that can be useful for public health practitioners who are working in Africa and for engaging more global users to the CTB, especially in areas where community health and development resources are needed. For example, the first author has written about how the Ministry of Public Health and Sanitation worked within Komo, Kenya to build trust within the community through Community Dialogue Days (CDDs). Led by community members, CDDs are an opportunity for discussions between partner organization leads, local government officials, and the community about their most pressing needs. This is an innovative approach that can be adopted by other communities in Africa and around the world to reach their public health goals.

In the summer of 2012, Dr. Davison Munodawafa invited the Africa CTB team to a six-week WHO Health Promotion Internship in Nairobi, Kenya, under the leadership of Dr. Kristine Kisia, to further develop Africa-based examples. Undergraduate fellows Ithar Hassaballa and Cara Smith traveled to Kenya to collect examples for the CTB and, at the same time, share this resource with community organizations and community leaders. This particular Health Promotion Internship allowed for the collection of Kenya-based examples ranging in issues (e.g., malaria, HIV) and topics (e.g., advocating for change, building leadership, and evaluation).

Upon her return from Kenya, Ithar Hassaballa shared lessons learned with the KU Kansas African Studies Center (KASC) and was awarded the African Community Health Fellowship in the summer of 2012 to write up the examples that were collected in Kenya. As a result of this internship, Africa-related case examples were produced for the Community Tool Box to ensure culturally appropriate use of the Toolkits. The CTB Toolkits are generalizable and adaptable, and diverse examples were included to make it easier for global communities to use the Toolkits. Africa-related CTB examples varied in topics (e.g., advocating for change on sexual violence, developing strategic and action plans on gender equity, building leadership through community health workers, etc.).

In the summer of 2013, the WHO Regional Office for Africa invited WHO CC staff to give a training on the Community Tool Box as a WHO AFRO Health Promotion Strategy to be used in Africa. As a Graduate Research Assistant in the midst of her MA/MPH degree at Kansas at that time, Ithar Hassaballa represented the WHO CC during the meeting. In the same meeting, WHO AFRO invited representatives from WHO country offices and representatives from Ministries of Health. More than fifty people represented a broad range of African nations, including the Nairobi, Kenya internship mentor, Dr. Kisia. Ithar Hassaballa delivered the presentation "The CTB as a Resource for Building Capacity" and a training titled "Increasing Community Participation" using the examples developed during the Kenya trip.

In the summer of 2014, the WHO CC was invited to the World Health Organization Consultative Meeting of Technical Resources on Addressing Key Determinants of Health in the African Region held in Port Louis, Mauritius. This time, WHO AFRO asked key staff to share their resources with WHO AFRO. Ithar Hassaballa delivered two presentations: "Addressing Specific Problems in Public Health Using the CTB Troubleshooting Guide" and "The WHO CC-based Monitoring and Evaluation (M&E) System." The CTB presentation focused on addressing specific problems, such as facing opposition, unintended outcomes, and not having enough leadership through the Troubleshooting Guide. The second presentation focused on the M&E system as a possible resource to monitor and evaluate the implementation of community and public health efforts in Africa. This trip was also an opportunity to learn from leading public health experts in Africa and further build trust and partnership between the Kansas and African partners, as well as opportunities to discuss interests and future opportunities.

The largest Ebola outbreak in history began March 2014, when the World Health Organization reported cases of Ebola Virus Disease (EVD) in Southeaster Guinea. The WHO published the Ebola Roadmap August 28, 2014, a few months after the Mauritius meeting. This document served as an action plan to address the Ebola outbreak in West Africa. Tasked with evaluating the Ebola response effort, the WHO Regional Office for Africa needed help. Because of the already established trust and relationship with the WHO CC and the available M&E capabilities there, WHO AFRO asked their partners in Kansas to work with them in evaluating the implementation of the Ebola response effort. The Ebola response effort focused on social mobilization, community engagement, and health promotion. The WHO CC team, led by Hassaballa and Dr. Fawcett, designed and developed an M&E system with WHO AFRO partners to ensure that the system had the ability to collect the information that would allow a broader audience to make sense of the activities that occurred to address Ebola within the selected counties in Liberia.

WHO AFRO staff members and a Liberia-based consultant, Ephraim Chiriseri, were trained to use this online documentation system to capture, code, characterize, and communicate the implementation of the Ebola response activities related to social mobilization. The Liberia-based consultant served as the primary observer, and a WHO CC staff member served as the secondary observer to code the activities and ensure accuracy of the definitions of activities. With technical support from the WHO CC, the WHO AFRO team: a) captured instances of community/organizational changes and services provided (e.g., which activity was implemented, when, by whom, toward what goal); b) coded by type of activity (e.g., whether a service provided or community change, using activity coding instruction); c) characterized the activity (e.g., by goal addressed, strategy used, or sector involved in the activity); and d) communicated progress using graphs of the unfolding of services provided over time and shared sense-making of the data (e.g., what are we seeing, what does it mean, and implications for adjustment). This process strengthened collaboration because there was constant communication between partners about the pandemic on the ground in Liberia. The WHO CC team provided support to colleagues on the ground facing the infectious disease outbreak and at the same time, the team in Liberia provided information about the outbreak and impact that only those on the ground could see and understand. For example, the community's beliefs around Ebola and preventive measures were impacted by misinformation about the disease found on social media (e.g., Whatsapp).

The collaborative process included making decisions on disseminating research emerging from the WHO AFRO team and the CCHD teams as part of the Ebola response effort. The Africa team suggested that because we had two target counties, it would be best to have at least two manuscripts. Through additional discussions, we decided to add a third overarching manuscript that the WHO AFRO team could lead as first authors and broadly share the lessons learned with the entire world, as the first publication coming directly from Africa on the Ebola outbreak. Most of the publications on the Ebola outbreak were coming from authors in Europe. Both collaborative teams decided that we would co-author all three transcripts. Because Ithar Hassaballa led the evaluation process, data collection, and meetings related to Lofa County, the team decided she could also draft the initial transcript as first author, while Charles Sepers led the Margibi County manuscript.

As a result of the collaborative partnership to evaluate the Ebola response effort, three manuscripts were eventually produced. The first paper is specific to Lofa County, Liberia (Hassaballa 2019), the second is unique to Margibi County, Liberia (Sepers 2018), and the third is a composite manuscript of both counties (Munodawafa 2017). In this chapter, I will focus on the Lofa County paper. A case study was developed on the participatory evaluation of the Ebola response effort in Lofa County, Liberia (Hassaballa 2019) that provided an overview of the Ebola outbreak and its consequences, describing the Ebola Response Roadmap, the need for monitoring and evaluation, and referencing WHO AFRO and WHO CC as collaborating partners. The three evaluation questions examined in the context of this case study were:

1. What was the pattern of implementation of the Ebola response effort in Lofa County?
2. Was implementation of the Ebola response effort associated with decreased incidence of Ebola in Lofa County?
3. What factors were associated with broader implementation of the Ebola response effort in Lofa County?

The pattern shows an acceleration of events, a deceleration, and then a steep acceleration until Ebola cases came close to zero. The discussion section included the results of the sense-making discussions, restraining factors, methodological challenges, and lessons learned. As part of the sense-making dialogue, WHO AFRO partners helped WHO CC understand that Lofa County was the epicenter of the Ebola outbreak in August 2014. When local youth and women's groups joined Ebola survivors, traditional healers, and traditional leaders to address denial, fear, and panic, Ebola incidence decreased, and efforts were shifted to other affected areas.

Some of the lessons learned through the Ebola response effort included that 1) the WHO has the convening power to bring different partners together to address infectious diseases, 2) using an M&E system was important in understanding key activities that occurred within Liberia to get to zero Ebola cases, 3) community engagement was critical in bringing about community/system changes such as new programs, policies, and practices. For example, initially, those who passed away due to Ebola would be placed in black body bags. For the Muslim populations in Lofa County, this went against their burial traditions since Muslims wrap their dead in a white cloth before burial. To address this cultural and religious need, WHO engaged partners so that white body bags were available. Because of this change, Muslim families engaged in safe burial practices. The final lesson learned was that intervention required sustained and coordinated action from all partners on the ground. The lessons learned from the Lofa

County Case study were used to control the spread of Ebola in Guinea. One such lesson that improved work in Guinea was the importance of the engagement of the local people, especially youth and women's groups, Ebola survivors, religious leaders, traditional leaders, and radio media. Engaging leaders was important in ensuring the public received accurate information on Ebola and protective behaviors to ensure safety. These groups were crucial in addressing denial, fear, and panic within Lofa County, Liberia, by organizing community-wide health promotion and disease prevention events.

In 2015, the authors participated in the University College London's Health and Society Summer School on the Social Determinants of Health program, led by Dr. Michael Marmot, then chair of the World Health Organization's Commission on the Social Determinants of Health and President of the World Medical Association. We were introduced to the topic of the social gradient—no matter which country a person is from, their health is directly impacted by their socioeconomic status. Discussions on the social gradient, behavior-environment relationships, and health justice inspired Ruaa Hassaballa-Muhammad's research on the impact of a national nurses' strike in Kenya on early infant HIV/AIDS diagnosis outcomes, which led to our later development of the Action Toolkit.

According to the United Nations Association for International Development, in Kenya, 120,000 children have HIV/AIDS. Only 65 percent of HIV-infected children estimated to need antiretroviral therapy (ART) are receiving it (UNAIDS 2016 – please clarify the reference). These challenges are heightened by social disruptions and inequity caused by low wages for healthcare workers at a time when they are overworked (Okeyo 2017). From June to November of 2017, a national nurses' strike caused a public health crisis in Kenya. Extremely low wages led 20,000 nurses to stop work and demand higher wages. A major impact of the strike was on prenatal services and maternal care, resulting in maternity mortality doubling during that time (Merab, 2017). For her project, early HIV/AIDS infant diagnosis outcomes at three Kenyan government hospitals were analyzed between June to November 2016 and June to November 2017 to determine the impact the strike had on early infant diagnosis services and outcomes. Specific outcomes compared for significant differences pre- and post-strike were a) age at infant testing for HIV, b) laboratory turnaround times and, c) initiation of antiretroviral therapy. The data was analyzed from the HIV Infant Tracking System (HITSystem), a web-based intervention utilizing algorithm-based provider prompts and text messaging to patients to track HIV-exposed infants through completion of early infant diagnosis outcomes services (Finocchario-Kessler 2014). The HITSystem is used to support receipt of complete early infant diagnosis services (including return of PCR test results to the hospital, mother notification of test results, and retesting at nine- and eighteen-months among HIV-negative infants or ART initiation among HIV-positive infants) and optimize turnaround times for key services (processing of PCR samples, mother notification of test results, and ART initiation). The study suggests that while the nurses' strike may not have significantly impacted early infant diagnosis outcomes, early infant diagnosis outcomes may be significantly improved at individual hospitals if private funding and resources are available. In addition, this study suggests that social disruption may decrease the number of infants able to seek life-saving care.

The African Health Action Toolkit

Through this evaluation research, we found that addressing social determinants of health in Africa is a major factor in ensuring that a similar outbreak does not occur in the future. To address the social determinants of health, building the capacity of a diverse and distributed workforce to address critical issues such as access to safe food, clean water, safe housing, transportation, education, healthcare, and the ability to generate income is needed. To ensure a diverse and distributed workforce, the WHO CC and WHO AFRO worked on an Africa-specific Action Toolkit to address social determinants of health by mobilizing, assessing, planning, taking action, evaluating, and sustaining various efforts. This Action Toolkit is the first of its kind that highlights key questions to consider, key action steps to take, and field notes from various African countries, WHO-related resources, and CTB resources. The WHO CC and WHO AFRO teams launched the Action Toolkit in September 2016 in Brazzaville, Congo. The Action Toolkit is an online resource that uses a framework for addressing social determinants of health that includes Mobilize, Assess, Plan, Act, and

Figure 2: WHO African Regional Office, WHO Collaborating Centre for Community Health and Development at the University of Kansas.

Evaluate/Sustain. The current website for the Action Toolkit is https://www.myctb.org/wst/who-afro-supports/Pages/Default.aspx. Each of the parts of the framework includes key questions to consider, core activities, field notes, resources from CTB and WHO, as well as other readings that can help with each section. (See Figure 2)

The African Health Action Toolkit has been used at the country-level to address social determinants of health, especially around education and economic development. There is a plan for English-speaking countries and Africa-based WHO Collaborating Centers to develop training using the Action Toolkit. WHO AFRO is giving African States an opportunity to implement efforts to address social determinants of health and include their field notes within the Action Toolkit website. Public health practitioners needed such resources to address social determinants of health nationally and locally to ensure stronger, healthier, more vibrant communities.

How Our Early Collaborations Prepared Us to Respond to COVID-19

Earlier collaborations between the WHO AFRO region and KU's WHO CC prepared the team to respond to COVID-19 when in January of 2020, the World Health Organization announced that the COVID-19 outbreak in China was caused by the 2019 Novel Coronavirus. As the COVID-19 pandemic swept throughout the world, it created a demand for information to help understand the response to COVID-19 and what enabled or impeded it. The World Health Organization Regional Office for Africa partnered with the KU WHO CC to support partners from Member States in using a participatory monitoring and evaluation system to document and systematically reflect on the COVID-19 response at the country level. A previous trusting relationship and familiarity with the Community Tool Box and M&E system enabled the WHO AFRO team to connect with the KU

WHO CC when support was needed to monitor and evaluate the response to COVID-19 in Africa.

The WHO AFRO's COVID-19 Response M&E team captured and communicated response activities based on reports from the forty-seven member countries. By reviewing documents and conducting key informant interviews, the M&E team documented over 5,000 COVID-19 response activities during the study period (February through December 2020). The team from the WHO CC at KU was formed by Ruaa Hassaballa-Muhammad, Dr. Stephen Fawcett, and Christina Holt. Hassaballa-Muhammad provided technical assistance by training country partners on the M&E online system and meeting weekly with WHO-AFRO partners to provide consultation and technical support. The WHO-AFRO team included Peter Phori, Noemie Nikiema, Cleph Siloukadila, and Deogratias Siku. They each brought expertise in data management, infectious disease, and understanding the local context of different African countries. Participatory sensemaking sessions with country partners helped to identify factors associated with increases or decreases in both new cases and response activities. Systematic reflection or sensemaking with the data strengthens shared understanding among partners about factors that enable or impede the response to COVID-19 and implications for adjustment. For example, in Senegal, partners reflected on what facilitated and impeded the response to COVID-19. Identified enabling factors that supported implementing the response in Senegal included involving religious leaders (May 2020), deploying awareness caravans (May), training health workers and border police officers (June), training surveillance teams (August), and intra-action review of COVID response (October). Factors identified as impeding the COVID-19 response activities in Senegal included challenges in implementing action plans at regional and district levels and in building capacity of the response team throughout the country. Some overall findings showed that when critical actors are involved in sensemaking, there is greater ownership of partner-generated recommendations for needed adjustments in the response.

Discussion and Conclusions

The collaborations between WHO CC (KU) and WHO AFRO have brought about greater opportunities to engage in comparative, community-engaged work, from which we can apply lessons learned to various different contexts globally. Community-based organizations have been able to share their work with the WHO CC and millions through the CTB.

This win-win collaboration also allowed the WHO CC to address issues collaboratively with WHO AFRO. The WHO CC was able to address a gap in the CTB: the inclusion of Africa-related health concerns, solutions, and examples. Further, when the Ebola outbreak began in West Africa, WHO AFRO partners in Africa knew about the M&E capabilities designed within the WHO CC. Without the M&E capabilities, the WHO CC could only encourage their colleagues at WHO AFRO, but because of the already available M&E resources, WHO CC was able to also offer guidance, technical consultation, and technical assistance. The work related to the Ebola effort gave the WHO CC an opportunity to serve and, at the same time, learn about the conditions for success when addressing an infectious outbreak. The launch of the Action Toolkit in Congo provided the WHO CC team an opportunity to understand how WHO AFRO operates, meet staff, and acknowledge the working conditions and barriers of working in low-resourced environments.

There were several ways that WHO AFRO and WHO CC built relationships including but not limited to regular virtual meetings on specific projects including M&E and collaborative manuscripts, annual in-person conferences, and keeping one another informed of opportunities for collaboration. Several conditions strengthened the collaboration of WHO

AFRO and WHO CC. The first condition is years of relationship building, beginning with the 7th Global Health Promotion conference in Kenya in 2009. The second condition is the presence of willing partners—as new colleagues take part in the WHO CC team and as new team members join WHO AFRO, everyone has been willing to work together. Third, the willingness to learn is a strength in the partnership—several times, team members had to do things that were new to both teams, but they were willing to learn by doing, which has been a major element of the collaboration's success. It was very important that we in the US collaborate with our Africa partners as learners. We do not go into the partnerships telling our partners what we think is important but instead ask about what our partners think is most important and then take action on recommendations. Fourth, flexibility is essential—WHO AFRO colleagues must sometimes travel to other countries to address various emergencies such as cholera outbreaks, dengue fever, and other health issues that take weeks at a time. Both teams have managed to stay the course by being flexible and beginning where they left off. One thing that helped the team get back on track is that the teams shared updates through e-mails and took notes in meetings to help fill in teammates unable to join a virtual meeting. Being flexible also included, for example, adapting the Action Toolkit to include British English since it is the preferred language in English-speaking African countries. Finally, programming for sustainability is critical, which is why building community members' capacity is crucial for continuing the work. The WHO CC has learned and continues to learn from its partners at WHO AFRO.

There were very few barriers to this collaboration. Reliable electricity and the Internet connection available to participating collaborators and communities was the most significant barrier to doing global work. Several meetings were rescheduled because Internet connection failed due to electricity or rain that resulted in internet outages. This was sometimes an obstacle to getting work done. For example, Dr. Fawcett and Ithar

Hassaballa experienced Internet connection issues firsthand during their trip to Congo to launch the Action Toolkit. Second, WHO AFRO handles high volumes of emergencies. Within a one-hour meeting in Congo, the WHO AFRO team was briefed on cholera outbreaks in three countries. Often, our partners traveled to places to address emergencies, which halted our collaborative work. The WHO CC, however, understands that there are emergencies and is willing to help as needed.

Our Lessons Learned for Team Members Participating in Global Health Collaborations

Over the last decade, the authors have gathered a list of lessons learned for global health collaboration based on their experiences working with WHO KU (CC) and WHO AFRO. First, seek multiple mentors and be prepared to serve as a mentor in your areas of expertise: It is important to connect early on and show up in spaces where like-minded individuals are going to be (e.g., for us, that was the Kansas African Studies Center (KASC), the United Nations Association). Mentorship can help mentees find opportunities and support. Second, we recommend accepting invitations and being open to new opportunities. Ithar Hassaballa was invited to a lunch with the multicultural scholars program, and Ruaa Hassaballa-Muhammad was invited to a course in London; both opportunities changed their trajectory. Third, work in a place that values equity, inclusion, and kindness or be an agent of change to promote them. At the WHO CC, the leaders created a safe environment where everyone was encouraged to bring their whole selves to work. At the same time, the leadership in Africa provided additional global health mentorships to the authors. Fourth, build authentic relationships with others for an extended period. Before Hassaballa joined the WHO CC, Dr. Fawcett and Dr. Munodawafa had a relationship and trust already built. When Hassaballa joined, it was time for her to start building connections with Dr. Munodawafa and Mr. Phori. This means that each side practices listening and cultivates relationship through check-in emails and having regular meetings to connect. Fifth, be empathetic and celebrate when the other side is celebrating. One of the most critical aspects of building global health partnerships is empathy to others and their conditions. We knew that our partners in Africa had many outside factors that impacted their ability to meet us more often. With that, we understood what they were going through and made sure we were as supportive as possible. At the same time, we celebrated their wins, whether they controlled a disease outbreak, presented at a conference, or published a paper. Sixth, honor everyone's brilliance, excellence, and expertise. We were meeting some of the most knowledgeable people in public health and global health, and although our approaches might be different, we needed to honor their expertise by seeking their input, asking questions, and seeking advice from them. This enriched not only our research and evaluation efforts but also our lives. Seventh, bring value. Had it not been for the leadership of our African partners, the Community Tool Box, the M&E system, and the already existing global health experiences, the partnership would have been limited. Always have cultural humility in understanding the value others bring, while understanding the value you bring and how that helps others meet their needs.

To conclude, Africans can solve Africa-based challenges when there are opportunities and resources. We do not believe in a broken public health system in Africa. We believe that the historical, structural, and economic factors impacting Africa are tremendous, but with collaborative efforts such as this one, Africa and the globe will succeed in addressing their health issues. Despite the historical, structural, and political challenges, African communities are innovative and resilient. African public health leaders have mentorship capabilities and wisdom to share with young public health professionals from around the globe.

Works Cited

African Health Action Toolkit. 2016. Accessed Feb. 7, 2023. https://who-afro.ctb.ku.edu/.

Chinman, Matthew, Gordon Hannah, Abraham Wandersman, Patricia Ebener, Sarah B. Hunter, Pamela Imm, Jeffrey Sheldon. 2005. "Developing a community science research agenda for building community capacity for effective preventive interventions." *American Journal of Community Psychology* 35, no. 3-4: 143-57.

Community Tool Box. n.d. Tools to change our world. Accessed Feb. 7, 2023. http://ctb.ku.edu/en.

Cousins, J. Bradly and Elizabeth Whitmore. 1998. "Framing participatory evaluation." *New Directions for Evaluation* 80: 5-23.

Fawcett, Stephen B., Renée Boothroyd, Jerry A. Schultz, Vincent T. Francisco, Valorie Carson, and Roderick Bremby. 2003. "Building Capacity for Participatory Evaluation Within Community Initiatives." *Journal of Prevention & Intervention in the Community* 26, no. 2: 21-36.

Fawcett, Stephen B., Vincent T. Francisco, Jerry A. Schultz. 2004. "Understanding and Improving the Work of Community Health and Development." In *Theory, basic and applied research, and technological applications in behavior science*, edited by Jose Burgos and Emilio Ribes, 209-42. Guadalajara, Mexico: Universidad de Guadalajara.

Fawcett, Stephen B., Vincent T. Francisco, Jerry A. Schultz, Bill Berkowitz, Thomas J. Wolff, and Genevieve Nagy. 2000. "The Community Tool Box: A Web-based resource for building healthier communities." *Public Health Reports* 115: 274–78.

Fawcett, Stephen B., Jerry A. Schultz, Vincent Thomas Francisco, Bill Berkowitz, Thomas J. Wolff, Paul W. Rabinotitz, Christina Marie Holt, Jami A. Jones. 2008. "Using Internet technology for capacity development in communities: The case of the Community Tool Box."

In Strategies of Community Intervention, edited by Jack Rothman, John
L. Erlich, and John E. Tropman, 7th ed. 263–281. Peosta, IA: Eddie
Bowers Publishing Co.

Fawcett, Steven B., Theodore D. Sterling, K. J. Harris, and Adrienne
Paine-Andrews. 1998. *Evaluating Community Efforts To Prevent
Cardiovascular Disease.* Collingdale, PA; Diane Publishing Co.

Fawcett, Steven, Palitha Abeykoon, Monica Arora, Madhumita Dobe,
Lark Galloway-Gilliam, Leandris Liburd, and Davison Munodawafa.
2010. "Constructing an action agenda for community empowerment
at the 7th Global Conference on Health Promotion in Nairobi."
Global Health Promotion 17, no. 4: 52-56.

Finocchario-Kessler, Sarah, Brad J. Gautney, Samoel Khamadi, Vincent
Okoth, Kathy Goggin, Jennifer K. Spinler, Anne Mwangi et al. 2014.
"If you text them, they will come: using the HIV infant tracking
system to improve early infant diagnosis quality and retention in
Kenya." *AIDS (London, England)* 28, no. 3: 313.

Francisco, Vincent T., Adrienne L. Paine, and Stephen B. Fawcett. 1993.
"A methodology for monitoring and evaluating community health
coalitions." *Health Education Research* 8, no. 3: 403-16.

Hassaballa, Ithar, Fawcett, Stephen, Sepers Jr., Charles, et al. 2019.
"Participatory monitoring and evaluation of Ebola response activities
in Lofa County, Liberia: Some lessons learned." *International Quarterly
of Community Health Education* 40, no 1: p. 57-66.

Leung, Margaret W., Irene H. Yen, and Meredith Minkler. 2004.
"Community based participatory research: a promising approach for
increasing epidemiology's relevance in the 21st century." *International
Journal of Epidemiology* 33, no. 3: 499-506.

Marmot, Michael. 2005. "Social determinants of health inequalities." *The
Lancet* 365, no. 9464: 1099-1104.

Morin, Rich. 2013. "The most (and least) culturally diverse countries in the world." Accessed Feb. 7, 2023. https://www.pewresearch.org/fact-tank/2013/07/18/the-most-and-least-culturally-diverse-countries-in-the-world/.

Munodawafa, Davison, Moeti, Matshidiso Rebecca, PHORI, Peter Malekele, et al. 2018. "Monitoring and evaluating the Ebola response effort in two Liberian communities." *Journal of Community Health* 43, no 2: 321-27.

Okeyo, S. M., A. K. Karani, and E. Matheka. 2017. "Challenges of technological trends in nursing and coping strategies by nurses at Kenyatta National Hospital." *East African Medical Journal* 94, no. 11: 960-71.

Phori, Peter Malekele, Stephen Fawcett, Noemie Nikiema Nidjergou, Cleph Silouakadila, Ruaa Hassaballa, and Deogratias Kakule Siku. "Participatory Monitoring and Evaluation of the COVID-19 Response in the Africa Region." *Health Promotion Practice* (2022): 15248399221095524.

Sepers Jr, Charles E., Fawcett, Stephen B., Hassaballa, Ithar, et al. 2019. "Evaluating implementation of the Ebola response in Margibi County, Liberia." *Health Promotion International* 34, no 3: 510-18.

Smith, Ben J., Kwok Cho Tang, and Don Nutbeam. 2006. "WHO Health Promotion Glossary: new terms." *Health Promotion International* 21, no. 4: 340-45.

World Health Organization Collaborating Centre for Community Health and Development. Accessed Feb. 7, 2023. https://communityhealth.ku.edu/who-collaborating-centre.

World Health Organization: Regional Office for Africa. 2013. Health Promotion Strategy for the African Region. Accessed Feb. 7, 2023. https://www.afro.who.int/sites/default/files/2017-06/Health%20Promotion%20Strategy%20inside%20English.pdf.

World Health Organization: Regional Office for Africa. 2014. The health

of the people, what works: The African Regional Health
Report 2014. Accessed Feb. 7, 2023. http://apps.who.int/iris/
bitstream/10665/137377/4/9789290232612.pdf.

WHO Regional Office for Africa. 2022. Accessed Feb. 7, 2023. https://
www.afro.who.int/

6

Mental Health During the Pandemic – Promoting Healthy Coping Strategies

Yvette G. Flores, *University of California, Davis*

Abstract:

The COVID-19 pandemic brought to light the health disparities diverse Latinx groups experience. In particular, the systemic barriers that limit access to mental health services and the stigma associated with seeking mental health care increased the risk for anxiety and depression among essential workers who faced high risk of contagion, as well as students whose life was altered radically, and older adults who faced increased isolation. This essay provides an intersectional analysis of the impact of COVID-19 on Latinx communities and explores decolonial strategies rooted in social justice and culturally attuned interventions that mobilize community cultural wealth and ancestral knowledge to promote mental health among Latinx youth and adults. Utilizing examples of teaching during the pandemic, consultation with parent groups, workshops to organizations, and psychotherapy sessions, we illustrate specific self-care strategies that utilize existing networks of support, rituals, traditions, and adaptive ways of coping to negotiate the pandemic, grieve the multiple losses experienced, and mobilize resilience.

The global pandemic that has caused millions of deaths, illness, and disability has been declared endemic as of this writing. The COVID-19 pandemic in the United States made visible the health disparities that have long affected Black, Indigenous, and other People of Color (BIPOC), who experienced greater rates of infection and death than white United Statians (Office of Minority Health, OMH 2021). The impact of the pandemic on physical health has been well documented. Data regarding the mental health impact of the pandemic is beginning to emerge, with evidence of significant increases in rates of anxiety, depression, trauma reactions, and complicated bereavement among children, youth, and adults (OMH 2021). Although the virus did not discriminate across race, ethnicity, sexuality, or gender lines, rates of infection and mortality data made visible risk factors that disproportionately affected BIPOC. This essay reviews some of these risk factors and addresses the need for mobilizing cultural protective factors to heal from the mental health sequelae of the pandemic among Latinxs.

I am a Central American immigrant who came to the United States as an adolescent; I have spent the last 34 years as a university professor and the last 36 years providing mental health services primarily to Latinx immigrants, refugees, and asylum seekers, as well as Chicanxs and US-born Latinxs. My educational and class privilege allowed me to work from home during the pandemic, teach classes online, and offer support to students, clients, colleagues, and friends. I offer examples of my work during the pandemic to illustrate how we negotiated our physical and mental health as we also struggled with anxiety, grief, and loss, yet attempted to remain hopeful.

Latinxs and COVID-19

Between March 2020 and September 2022, I treated two dozen therapy clients and evaluated 65 Latinx immigrants in immigration proceedings. Of these individuals and families only 2 have not had COVID-19 or its variants. All of my clients are working-class, essential workers, or adults who stayed home to oversee their children's on-line schooling. They range in age from 6 to 84. The two families that have not become ill had children under the age of 3 and did not visit any relatives or work outside the home for two years. The rest became infected in 2020 and 2021. A few became ill when their children returned to school in person and were exposed to the virus. Only one family was not vaccinated for fear of the vaccine. The Lopez family lost a father to COVID-19 in February 2021 and two other older relatives in Mexico. Mrs. Lopez became clinically depressed after her father died but had not received mental health services as she has no health insurance. The Lopez family as several others in my practice, have had COVID-19 twice.

Latinxs currently comprise 24.9% of COVID-19 cases in the United States, second only to Whites (53.6%), according to CDC data on health equity and cases on April 19, 2022 (CDC COVID Data Tracker 2022). The high rates of infection occur across all states in the Union, where Latinxs are only second to whites; in California, which is 39.3% Latinx, they constituted 47.6% of COVID-19 cases as of March 30, 2022. COVID-19-associated hospitalizations also have been higher among Latinxs (McCormack 2021). Similarly, Latinxs are only second to whites in US COVID-19 deaths; 16.2% of US COVID-19 deaths are among Latinxs, according to the CDC (2020).

Latinxs died at greater rates than the other ethnic groups in every age group examined: 31.3% of these deaths were among Latinxs 0-24 years of age; much higher than the other ethnic groups; 32.2% were among Latinxs ages 25-34; in the 35-44 age range, Latinxs represented 33.8% of deaths. Of deaths in the 45-54 age group, 29.4% were among Latinxs; likewise, 22.4% of deaths in the 54-64 age group were among Latinxs. Among older Latinxs, 16.9% of the deaths in the 65-74 age group were among Latinxs, and 12.8% of deaths in the 75-84 age group were Latinxs. Among those 85 and older, 9.3% of the deaths were Latinxs (CDC 2022).

As of March 16, 2022, 159,531 Latinxs had died due to COVID-19, compared to 138,083 Blacks, 622,483 Whites; 30,444 Asian Americans,

10,662 American Indian/Alaska Native, and 2,081 Native Hawaiian/ Pacific Islander. These disparities also were manifested in all states where race/ethnicity of COVID-19 deaths were reported. In California, where Latinxs constitute 39.3% of the population, 46.2% of deaths were among Latinxs.

Annually, CDC researchers compile and analyze data to predict the number of deaths that will occur in the coming year. The number of mortalities that go over this initial estimate, or the difference between the observed numbers of deaths in specific time periods and expected numbers of deaths in the same time periods, are known as excess deaths (McCormack 2021). Looking at deaths in 2020 compared with predicted deaths, researchers found that US Latinxs suffered double the excess deaths per 100,000 people compared to their white peers. With COVID-19 as a cause, excess deaths per 100,000 persons from March to December 2020 among Blacks and Latinxs were more than double those among whites. This finding represents profound racial/ethnic disparities in excess deaths in the United States in 2020 during the COVID-19 pandemic. Laster-Pirtle (2020) describes this reality as racial capitalism, a manifestation of structural racism.

Although the vaccination data vary by state, with some states reporting greater hesitancy among Latinxs to get vaccinated, public health campaigns targeting Latinx subgroups have been successful in reducing hesitancy and increasing vaccination rates. The Kaiser Family Foundation (Ndugga et al. 2022) reports that Latinxs make up a larger share of vaccinated people (21%) and people who recently received a vaccination (35%) compared to their share of the total population (19%). The differential rates of infection, hospitalization, and death among Latinxs are explained in terms of longstanding health disparities and the context of Latinx health.

The Context of Latinx Health

Latinxs in the United States are a culturally, racially, and ethnically diverse population who may identify as indigenous, Afro Latinx, mestizo, or white. They may include individuals and families that have always been on the lands that now comprise the Southwestern United States. For many Latinxs, their ancestors did not migrate. US western expansion and the Treaty of Guadalupe Hidalgo (1848) incorporated them. Some migrated during the Gold Rush or as part of the Bracero Program and settled in various states. Others migrated in the 20th Century due to economic and political instability in Mexico, Central America, the Caribbean, and South America. More recent Latinx immigrants have fled gang wars or natural disasters from Honduras, Nicaragua, and El Salvador. Indigenous Central Americans have fled religious, political, or ethnic persecution, including large numbers of Mayans from Guatemala and unaccompanied minors from Honduras (Alvarado et al. 2017). Each of these groups bring with them their language, culture, traditions, and health practices that are often marginalized and misunderstood in the US context. However, those cultural practices can serve as sources of healing in times of crisis.

The extant literature portrays Latinxs, in particular immigrants, as having equal to or better health outcomes than more economically privileged non-Hispanic whites. Some scholars refer to this as the Latinx Health Paradox (Markides and Coreil 1986) since the majority of Latinxs face multiple structural barriers, including underemployment, lower educational attainment, and lower rates of health insurance, as well as persistent experiences of discrimination, racism, sexism, classism and pervasive microaggressions that contribute to "minority stress" (Meyer 2003). Despite these potentially adverse conditions, many Latinxs live longer than their non-Hispanic white counterparts. The relative health of Latinx immigrants is explained in part by the protective factors many immigrants bring with them, including strong family ties and collectivist values that promote a community orientation. Likewise, Latinx immigrants have lower rates of substance misuse and smoking, as well as better nutrition. However, these protective factors begin to decrease within a few years of living in the US By the second generation, Latinxs' health status is comparable to, or worse than, other ethnic groups. A more detailed analysis of the Latinx health context finds high rates of hypertension, diabetes, and some forms of cancer (OMH 2021), particularly among older adults.

The health of Latinxs is often shaped by factors such as language or cultural barriers, lack of access to preventive care, and lack of health insurance. The Centers for Disease Control and Prevention (2022) has cited some of the leading causes of illness and death among Latinxs, including heart disease, cancer, unintentional injuries (accidents), stroke, and diabetes. Some other health conditions and risk factors that significantly affect Latinxs are asthma, chronic obstructive pulmonary disease, HIV/AIDS, obesity, suicide, and liver disease. For example, Latinxs have higher rates of obesity than non-Hispanic whites; the incidence of childhood obesity among Mexican Americans, for example, is concerning (de la Torre et al. 2013). There also are disparities among Latinx subgroups. For instance, while the rate of low birthweight infants is lower for the total Latinx population in comparison to non-Hispanic whites, Puerto Ricans have a low birthweight rate that is almost twice that of non-Hispanic whites. Puerto Ricans also suffer disproportionately from asthma, HIV/AIDS, and infant mortality, while Mexican Americans suffer disproportionately from diabetes. These underlying medical conditions have been used to explain the high death rate among Latinx adults with COVID-19. However, a focus on underlying health conditions initially obscured some of the other inequalities Latinxs face that contributed to the high rates of infection, severe illness, and death.

Significant contributors to infection are associated with employment. People of color disproportionately work in front line jobs or are deemed essential workers. The majority of Latinxs are essential workers – construction, service sector, hospital and clinic custodians, food workers, landscapers, and farmworkers – who could not shelter in place. Many Latinxs reside in multigenerational households and high-density dwellings where the spread of the virus was at times unpreventable despite precautions taken. In addition, in the early stages of the pandemic, significant misinformation affected Latinx communities. Distrust of the government and the confused messaging regarding the severity of the pandemic may have increased the risk of infection.

Most important is the fact that Latinxs of various national origins and generational levels experience significant health disparities. Latinxs have the highest uninsured rates of any racial or ethnic group within the United States. In 2019, the Census Bureau reported that 50.1% of Latinxs had private insurance coverage, as compared to 74.7% for non-Hispanic whites. Among Latinx subgroups, insurance coverage varied as follows: 47.9% of Mexican origin persons, 56.3% of Puerto Ricans (who are US citizens), 57.4% of Cubans, and 41.7% of Central Americans. In 2019, 36.3% of all Latinxs had Medicaid or public health insurance coverage, as compared to 34.3% for non-Hispanic whites. Public health insurance coverage varied among subgroups: 36.4% of Mexicans, 43.7% of Puerto Ricans, 33.7% of Cubans, and 33.0% of Central Americans. Those without health insurance coverage varied among subgroups as well: 20.3% of Mexicans, 8.0% of Puerto Ricans, 14.0% of Cubans, and 19.4% of Central Americans. In 2019, 18.7% of the Latinx population was not covered by health insurance, as compared to 6.3% of the non-Hispanic white population (OMH 2021). The limited access to health insurance often is associated with employment characteristics, lack of resources to purchase private insurance, and lack of eligibility to obtain insurance among undocumented immigrants.

Despite the lack of health care access, according to the Census Bureau projections, the 2020 life expectancies at birth for Latinxs are 82.1 years, with 84.2 years for women, and 79.9 years for men, which is higher than for non-Hispanic whites. They have projected life expectancies of 80.6 years, with 82.7 years for women, and 78.4 years for men (OMH 2021). Although Latinxs may have a longer life span than non-Hispanic whites, their quality of life may be compromised by illness. The long-term effects of COVID-19 are not yet understood.

Latinx Mental Health

Doña Rosa,* a 52-year-old Salvadorean immigrant, worked as a janitor of a large office building prior to the pandemic. In March of 2020, she became ill with flu-like symptoms. When she told her employer that she was not feeling well, he told her to go home and not come back. He failed to tell her that several employees in the building had developed similar symptoms. One of the workers was hospitalized and diagnosed with COVID-19. Ill, uninsured, and unemployed as the building closed shortly after she became ill, Doña Rosa fell into a deep depression. Her daughter, a former student of mine, called me to seek information on how best to help out her mother. Her daughter tried to find mental health services for her mother; however, the shelter-in-place order limited the availability of services. Moreover, Doña Rosa only spoke Spanish and was not comfortable discussing her sadness on the phone with a stranger. Her situation was not unique.

While the pandemic affected the mental health of all citizens, with 1 in 5 adults developing a pandemic-related mental disorder (Simon 2021), according to the CDC (2021), Latinxs surveyed reported higher rates of depression, substance use, and suicidal thoughts. Over 40% of Latinx adults surveyed reported symptoms of depression during the pandemic. They reported symptoms of current depression 59% more frequently than non-

* Client names have been anonymized throughout this paper.

Hispanic White adults. They also experienced suicidal thoughts/ideation two to four times as much as other demographic groups and increased or newly initiated substance use twice as much. The pandemic threatened the sobriety of Latinxs in recovery (McKnight et al. 2020). Latinxs with histories of trauma experienced an exacerbation of hyperalertness and other trauma symptoms.

The CDC survey asked respondents about "social determinants of health" including: stress and worry about possible job loss, ability to obtain needed health care, not having enough food, and housing instability. Latinx adults expressed more stress about not having enough food (22.7%) or stable housing (20.7%) than White adults (11.9% and 9.2%, respectively) (McKnight et al. 2020). These were some of Doña Rosa's concerns: how would she find another job to support her children since she had "no papers," that is, as an unauthorized immigrant.

Nativity and immigration status are important factors to consider with regard to the incidence and prevalence of psychiatric disorders, as well as community and individual responses to pandemic-related distress. The mental health of immigrant Latinxs decreases with increased US residence (Secretariat of the Interior/National Population Council CONAPO 2017). After six years or more of living in the US, Latinxs report high rates of mood and anxiety disorders, which often are associated with stressful life circumstances, including acculturative stress. All indicators also find higher rates of intimate partner and family violence during the pandemic, which heightened the risk for injury and mental health problems for women and children. Although the need for services is high at this time, mental health service utilization by Latinxs is limited (Bridge, Andrews, and Deen 2012).

A number of explanations for the underutilization of mental health services are offered in the literature (Bridge, Andrews and Deen 2012; Alegría et al. 2007); primary among these are lack of access to mental health services due to cost and poor health insurance coverage. Other structural factors also are identified, including lack of Latinx and/or bilingual providers, lack of cultural humility among providers, and discriminatory practices. Stigma associated with mental illness also can be a deterrent to help-seeking among some Latinxs (Flores 2013). Moreover, during the pandemic, most mental health services were offered virtually or by phone. Latinxs without access to computers or smartphones had difficulty accessing these services when available. In my own practice, my Spanish-speaking clients did not want to have sessions online or by phone and preferred to wait until we could meet in person. Many of my English-speaking or more acculturated clients opted for virtual or phone sessions and have preferred to continue meeting that way when in-person sessions resumed.

It is important to note that when culturally congruent mental health services are provided, Latinxs will utilize services if they are accessible and affordable. Tervalon and Murray-Garcia (1998) stress the importance of cultural humility in the delivery of health services to Latinx. An essential consideration is recognizing the diversity of Latinxs and the impact of stress on the well-being of Latinx individuals.

Stress and Well-Being

As stated above, many Latinxs experienced significant stress during the pandemic due to work and housing insecurity, and fear of contracting the virus and bringing it home to their loved ones. Social stress is produced not only by personal events, but also by conditions of living related to their social context and Latinx intersectional identities—gender, sexuality, nativity, social class, and race. Social stress disproportionately affects people belonging to minoritized groups who are stigmatized for various reasons, such as their economic situation, race, gender, background, or aspects of their sexuality. Marginalized groups experience both macro and micro-aggressions that can compromise their physical and emotional well-being.

Significant research conducted with sexual minorities (Iniewicz et al. 2017) sheds light on important areas of intervention to support adaptive coping during and post-pandemic.

Minority Stress refers to the chronically high levels of stress faced by members of stigmatized minority groups. It may be caused by a number of factors, including poor social support, low socioeconomic status, and interpersonal prejudice and discrimination.

Studied extensively with members of LGBTQ communities (Iniewicz et al. 2017), understanding these factors is essential to promoting well-being.

Among BIPOC, additional risk factors to mental health include gender and class.

For the working class, life and work are often synonymous (Bernal and Alvarez 1983); the impact of unemployment on Latinx men is associated with depression, anxiety, and substance misuse (Flores et al. 2019; Flores et al. 2022). Latinx men will often go to work despite the risks inherent in the jobs they have (construction, farm work, for example) and during the pandemic because of their perceived obligation to fulfill the cultural and class mandate to be the family provider. Single mothers had no option but to work and manage their children's at-home education, reporting high levels of stress. As noted above, despite feeling very ill with fever and difficulty breathing, Doña Rosa wanted to return to work to support her children and provide care for her grandchildren. Latinx children and youth also have reported significant increases in anxiety and depression, and difficulties with returning to school. Older Latinxs who were isolated from their families experienced cognitive decline and increased incidence of depression (McKnight-Eily et al. 2021).

Although Latinxs experience disparities regarding mental health, a number of protective factors may mitigate COVID-19 related stress and psychiatric disorders. Several studies (Gonzalez 2020) point to resilience among immigrants, in particular, stoicism as a way to cope with adversities, religious faith, networks of support, and positive ethnic, racial, and sexual identity (especially for queer youth of color) as critical protective factors.

In addition, a number of factors may mediate between stress and coping and exacerbate stress. Among these factors are internalized racism and controlling images that denigrate Latinx, which may increase the impact of pandemic-related stress. Controlling images are more serious and pervasive than stereotypes (Crenshaw 2017). They are gender-specific – "the angry Black Woman," the loud Latina, perception of Black males as criminals, Latinx men as burros, beasts of burden, bad hombres, immigrants as criminals or carriers of the virus, and creators of "anchor babies." These controlling images adversely impact the mental health of minoritized individuals and may have increased the emotional distress of Latinxs in the first year of the pandemic due to the rhetoric coming from those in power at the time. Such rhetoric resulted in increased discrimination against BIPOC and hate crimes against Asian Americans and Latinxs who were assumed to be immigrants.

Promoting Latinx Well-Being and Coping During the Pandemic

As an educator and community clinical psychologist working in both educational and mental health contexts for over 30 years, I was called upon to respond to the emotional distress of students and clients alike during the pandemic. Informed by Mujerista (Bryant-Davis and Comas-Diaz 2016) and Liberation Psychologies (Martín-Baró 1994), I focused on assessing sources of distress, support systems, and coping strategies with students and clients. As the pandemic also coincided with the very public murder of George Floyd and other BIPOC, it was critical to address anti-Black racism and trauma symptoms in my Chicanx Studies psychology classes as well as in therapy sessions.

Most of the students in the department where I teach are Latinx or BIPOC, first-generation, and from working-class backgrounds. Our faculty are also Latinx; most are first-generation college graduates and come from diverse backgrounds (urban, farm work, rural); some of us are US-born, and some of us are immigrants. Most are of Mexican origin. I am the only Central American faculty member. Our Department Chair and administrative team provided social, emotional, and logistical support to both faculty and students throughout the pandemic and were particularly attentive to older faculty members such as myself, who might be at greater risk of death if infected. In the Spring quarter of 2020, my colleagues switched from in-person to online teaching within days with the immense support of our chair and staff. I began to teach online in the fall of 2020.

As a professor teaching during the pandemic, I began each class taught synchronously online, and recorded for those unable to connect in real time, with a check-in. A survey was regularly administered by our department that assessed food availability, housing, current health status of the student and their family and roommates, if still living on campus. Thus, I had some information regarding the type of stress my students might be experiencing. Students who needed housing, food, or medical referrals were triaged to campus services. The lack of Latinx mental health providers presented a challenge, but our department staff tried to find community providers who could offer free or low-fee consultation. Two of us are licensed psychologists; thus, we could support our colleagues with other disciplinary trainings on how to approach students in crisis. Our campus also offered support through health services. I also encouraged students to become familiar with our state's COVID-19 resources and virtual online support services.

In each course I have taught since the pandemic began, we prioritized our emotional and physical well-being. During each class period, students were invited to break out into small groups to discuss social, academic, or emotional needs they were experiencing. We concluded each class period with a mindfulness practice and shared cultural practices that might be helpful, from prayer to home remedies, and healing rituals their grandparents, parents, or friends might utilize. At the end of each class period, students were invited to offer examples of how they navigated their multiple roles during the week. Many of our students had gone home when the campus shut down and thus were living with parents, siblings, and other relatives, helping out with household chores, working remotely, and attending classes. Students could write in the chat or unmute to speak. Once they shared, we tried to connect their strategy to cultural practices they might have learned at home or in the community. We kept a running list of strategies students could go back and utilize when stressful situations presented themselves. I also introduced breathing and mindfulness exercises for the last 5-10 minutes of class. Students from other cultural and racial backgrounds shared their own cultural rituals and found similarities with their Latinx classmates. We all learned from and offered support to each other. Many of our students had returned home during the pandemic and had to support the homeschooling of younger siblings, or join their parents in their essential work as janitors or landscapers to help supplement the family income or to take over their jobs if the parents became ill with COVID-19. Thus, they could not attend classes synchronously; we provided recordings and resources for them, as well as office hours via telephone. Some of our students reported having to do their homework or listen to lectures in a closet, given the background noise in their home, with siblings also taking courses online. The level of stress among most of our students was significant. Students shared and taught each other their practices, including the ways in which they offered gratitude, prayer, meditation, yoga, and mindfulness. They spoke about ancestor worship and how, in their cultural tradition, smudging and ceremony helped regain balance.

Course assignments encouraged the use of the arts to promote spiritual and emotional balance. Rather than writing papers, students had the option of using media, art, or music to demonstrate their mastery of Latinx psychology concepts. Some students shared spoken work performances reflecting the struggles the pandemic created for their families; others drew images of grief and strength they witnessed in their family. Utilizing concepts from identity theories, students wrote essays about their identity as a pandemic survivor.

Self-Care During the Pandemic

During times of crisis, it is particularly important to engage in self-care. As Latinxs from working-class backgrounds, especially for those of us who grew up in marginalized communities, taking time for ourselves to maintain our health and spiritual well-being may be difficult. We may have been socialized to prioritize others over our own well-being; this is particularly likely among Latinas raised in traditional families. Thus, in class, we examined our gender roles and the ways in which we needed to create space for ourselves without feeling guilty. As family caregivers, we need to nurture ourselves in order to refill our well. I argued that we may need to check out and disconnect from our family obligations, if only briefly, in order to connect to ourselves and determine what resources we had, what we needed, and where to get our needs met. This would make it easier to connect with others from a place of strength. Likewise, for those of us with histories of trauma, the uncertainties created by the pandemic might lead us to feel vulnerable and unsafe; we may then go into trauma mode. I invited the students to connect the theories they were learning to their experiences in the moment.

For those of us with histories of social, state, family, or intimate partner violence, it was crucial to prioritize our emotional, physical, and spiritual well-being to mobilize our resilience.

The students were invited to explore their cultural traditions, as these offered ways of balancing and healing. I also promoted balance through exercise, baking, cooking, reaching out to others, or isolating to ground and balance when needed.

My goal was to facilitate a connection to the community's cultural wealth (Yosso 2006) that each of us has. One way to do this is by drawing from our ancestral well, the conscious and unconscious resources and life lessons emerging from our ancestors' histories. In times of crisis, we can draw from the legacies, stories, and his/herstories of our elders and ancestors and transform our fears into opportunities. I invited students to examine where they drew their strength to continue working, keeping up with school, supporting their families, and helping their children's and siblings' distance learning. I shared with them stories of my ancestors; the men who crossed continents coming from Europe and Asia in the nineteenth century and came to the Americas seeking better opportunities, and the indigenous, mestiza, and Afro-Latinas who partnered with these men.

I shared with the students that one day when I was feeling particularly defeated and hopeless during the first few months of the pandemic, I was having trouble holding space for the pain and suffering of others while dealing with my own anxiety and grief, and I remembered the story of my children's paternal grandmother, Maria Hernandez, who survived the 1918 flu pandemic and crossed the Rio Grande after her husband, baby daughter, and parents had succumbed to the virus. A widow who lost almost her entire family, she walked to the border from Camargo, Tamaulipas, Mexico with her young son and ultimately settled in Texas. We do not know how she made that journey, what challenges she faced, because she never talked about it. I found her diary and related documents after her son was killed and the family had to close out the home. By this point, she was in a nursing home in the end stage of Alzheimer's disease. I organized her papers and shared them with her children. I saved the papers as well as her memory for many years, until that day. I reflected on her courage, her desire to save her son and provide him with a better life by making the arduous journey to the United States. I quickly got over my self-pity and focused on what I could do to support others – my students, family, friends, and therapy clients. I asked my students, what lessons of resilience could we learn from people like her? While studying the concept of resilience, for example, students interviewed family members about their migration to the US and identified their relatives' cultural resources that helped them cope. In this way, these students could dig into their ancestral well and find ways to cope with the pandemic in culturally syntonic ways. What stories could be told about them a hundred years from now when scholars study this pandemic?

In the fall of 2020, when Latinx cultural groups honored their dead, I invited students to build an altar in their homes honoring their ancestors and those lost to the pandemic. As they learned about health disparities and Latinx illness and death rates from COVID-19, they engaged in action research to educate members of their community about the virus and how to prevent contagion. For example, students organized to obtain and send masks and gloves to farmworkers in nearby communities with the support of a department faculty member. Students also gathered their family members who were essential workers and provided them with information regarding the importance of using protective equipment, masks, gloves, etc. They used video chat to connect to relatives in Mexico and Central America and offer them updated information. Through these efforts, the students felt more empowered, and their depression and anxiety lessened. We used the course content and their cultural capital to find solutions, in the moment, to their distress and to create positive change in their families and communities; for example students reported that they shared course material about the importance of ethnic/racial/cultural identity with younger siblings who were struggling with their own positionality, and talked to their parents about their experience as students so they could support each other in more direct ways. While at home, students felt that their parents expected them to focus on family needs and not their coursework. A Chicana student shared how she began to talk to her mother about the academic expectations she had to meet while being home as they were both preparing dinner. Her mother then asked her adult son who was not in school or working to step up and do more around the house because his sister had schoolwork to do (see McCormack 2021 for Latinx community-level responses to the pandemic).

Conclusions

The COVID-19 pandemic has taught us many lessons. In our isolation, those of us privileged enough to work from home found creative outlets, built virtual support networks, and found ways to remain connected. Those who continued working to keep the economy going sacrificed to feed the rest of us. We must not forget their sacrifice and that of all the first responders who tended to the sick, drove the ambulances, and cleaned the COVID-19 contaminated hospital rooms, corridors, and bathrooms. We academics, particularly those in health-related fields, must do more and must do better to address health disparities and safeguard the physical, emotional, and spiritual well-being of all citizens. In the months and years to come, we must continue to safeguard the physical and emotional health of children and youth whose education was disrupted by the pandemic. As health scholars, we must reflect on the lessons of this virus and strengthen our individual and community responses as we continue to work towards greater health parity for all. The health disparities affecting communities of color are visible and undeniable; we must address the systemic racism that creates and maintains these disparities. We must continue to train health scholars with cultural humility and a willingness to learn from and with community partners. Ultimately, we need to continue in dialogue with humanists and social scientists to learn from each other to be better and do better, as we are aiming to do in this book.

Works Cited

Alegría, Margarita, Norah Mulvaney-Day, Maria Torres, Antonio Polo, Zhun Cao, Glorisa Canino. 2007. "Prevalence of psychiatric disorders across Latino subgroups in the United States." *American Journal of Public Health* 97: 68–75.

Alvarado, Karina Oliva, Estrada, Alicia Ivonne, Ester E. Hernandez. 2017. *US Central Americans: Reconstructing Memories, Struggles, and Communities of Resistance.* Tucson: University of Arizona Press.

Bryant-Davis, Thema, and Lillian Comas-Diaz. 2016. *Womanist and Mujerista Psychologies: Voices of Fire, Acts of Courage.* Washington: American Psychological Association.

Center for Disease Control and Prevention. n.d. "Provisional Death Counts for Coronavirus Disease 2019." National Center for Health Statistics. Accessed January 27, 2023. https://www.cdc.gov/nchs/nvss/vsrr/covid19/index.htm.

Centers for Disease Control and Prevention. n.d. "Health Disparities: Race and Hispanic origin provisional death counts for coronavirus disease." National Center for Health Statistics. Accessed January 27, 2023. https://www.cdc.gov/nchs/nvss/vsrr/covid19/health_disparities.htm#RaceHispanicOrigin.

Centers for Disease Control and Prevention. n.d. COVID Data Tracker. Accessed January 27, 2023. https://covid.cdc.gov/covid-data-tracker/#datatracker-home.

Crenshaw, Kimberlé W. 2017. *On Intersectionality: Essential Writings.* New York, NY: The New Press.

de la Torre, Adela, Banafsheh Sadeghi, Richard D. Green, Lucia L. Kaiser, Yvette G. Flores, Carlos F. Jackson, Sara E. Schaefer, Ulfat Shaikh, Linda Whent. 2013. "Niños Sanos, Familia Sana: Mexican Immigrant Study Protocol for a Multifaceted CBPR intervention to combat childhood obesity in two rural California towns." *BMC Public Health* 13, no. 1033. Doi:10.1186/1471-2458-13-1033, http://www.biomedcentral.com/1471-2458/13/1033.

Flores, Yvette G. 2013. *Chicana and Chicano Mental Health: Alma, Mente y Corazón* (The Mexican Experience). Tucson: University of Arizona Press.

Flores, Yvette G., Lisceth Brazil-Cruz, Hector Rivera-Lopez, Rosa D. Manzo, Monica Siañez, and Erika I. Cervantes-Pacheco. 2019. "Aquí en Confianza (Here in Confidence): Narratives of Migration, Mental Health, and Family Reunification of Mexican Immigrant Men in the California Central Valley." In *Community-Based Participatory Research: Testimonios from Chicana/o Studies*, edited by Natalia Deeb-Sossa, 153-78. Tucson: University of Arizona Press.

Flores, Yvette G. 2022. "Finding Home / Haciendo Familia: Testimonios of Mexican Male Farmworkers in Central California." In *Latinx Belonging: Community Building and Resilience in the United States*, edited by Natalia Deeb-Sosa and Jennifer Bickham Mendez, 143-65. Tucson: University of Arizona Press.

Gonzalez, Elsa. 2020. "Foreword: understanding Latina/o resilience." *International Journal of Qualitative Studies in Education* 33, no.8: 791-95.

Iniewicz, Grzegorz, K. Salapa, Malgorzata Wrona, Natalia Marek. 2017. "Minority stress among homosexual and bisexual individuals - from theoretical concepts to research tools: The Sexual Minority Stress Scale." *Archives of Psychiatry and Psychotherapy* 3: 69–80.

Laster-Pirtle, Whitney N. 2020. "Racial Capitalism: A Fundamental Cause of Novel Coronavirus (COVID-19) Pandemic: Inequities in the United States." *Health Education and Behavior* 47, no. 4: 504-08.

Markides, Kyriakos S., and Jeannine Coreil. 1986. "The Health of Hispanics in the Southwestern United States: an Epidemiological Paradox." *Public Health Reports*, no.101: 253-65.

Martín-Baró, Ignacio. 1994. *Writings for a Liberation Psychology*. Cambridge: Harvard University Press.

McCormack, Josh. 2021. "Study: Latinos Suffered Highest Rate of COVID-19 Hospitalizations." Salud America!. Accessed January 27, 2023. https://salud-america.org/study-latinos-suffered-highest-rate-of-covid-19-hospitalizations/.

McKnight-Eily, Lela R., Cathrine A. Okoro, Tara W. Strine, Jorge Verlenden, NaTasha D. Hollis, Rashid Naji, Elizabeth W. Michell, Amy Board, Richard Puddy, and Craig Thomas. 2021. "Racial and Ethnic Disparities in the Prevalence of Stress and Worry, Mental Health Conditions, and Increased Substance Use Among Adults During the COVID-19 Pandemic — United States, April and May 2020." Accessed January 23, 2023. *MMWR Morbidity and mortality weekly report* 70 (5):162–66. doi:10.15585/mmwr.mm7005a3.

Meyer, Ilan H. 2003. "Prejudice, Social Stress, and Mental Health in Lesbian, Gay, and Bisexual populations: Conceptual Issues and Research Evidence. *Psychological Bulletin* 129(5): 674-97. https://doi.org/10.1037/0033-2909.129.5.674.

Ndugga, Nambi, Latoya Hill, Samantha Artiga, and Sweta Haldar. 2022. "Latest Data on COVID-19 Vaccination by race/ethnicity." Kaiser Family Foundation. Accessed January 27, 2023. https://www.kff.org/coronavirus-covid-19/issue-brief/latest-data-on-covid-19-vaccinations-by-race-ethnicity/.

Office of Minority Health [OMH] 2021. The Impact of COVID-19 in Latinos: What can we do to move forward? Accessed November 30, 2021. Minorityhealth.hss.gov.

Secretaria of the Interior/National Population Council (CONAPO), 2017. *Migration & Health: Reflections and challenges about the health of migrants*. Accessed January 27, 2023. https://www.gob.mx/conapo/archivo/documentos?idiom=es.

Simon, Sarah. 2021. "CDC: Latinx Community Hit Hard by COVID Mental Health Issues." *Very well health.* Accessed January 27, 2023. https://www.verywellhealth.com/latinx-mental-health-issues-cdc-report-5185748.

Tervalon, Melanie, and J Murray-Garcia. 1998. "Cultural Humility Versus Cultural Competence: A Critical Distinction in Defining Physician Training Outcomes in Multicultural Education." *Journal of health care for the poor and underserved* 9(2): 117-25.

Yosso, Tara J. 2006. "Whose culture has capital? A critical race theory discussion of community cultural wealth." *Race Ethnicity and Education* 8(1): 69-91. DOI: 10.1080/1361332052000341006.

Notes on Contributors

Co-Editors

Dalia Magaña is an Associate Professor of Spanish Linguistics at the University of California, Merced. Her research focuses on using metaphors in health discourse, such as cancer and mental health, improving healthcare communication with Spanish speakers, and developing intentional language pedagogy. Her studies have been published in *Academic Medicine, Patient Education & Counseling*, and *Health Communication* and raise awareness about the role of interpersonal language in improving healthcare communication with local communities of Spanish speakers. Her first book, *Building Confianza: Empowering Latinx Patients Through Transcultural Interactions* (2021), argues that effective doctor–patient communication in Spanish requires practitioners who have transcultural knowledge of Latinos' values and sociolinguistic awareness of their language use. In collaboration with a team of linguists, she co-authored a book, *Health Disparities and the Applied Linguist* (forthcoming), which bridges theory and practice to demonstrate how applied linguists are uniquely positioned to make vital contributions toward advancing health equity in the US.

Christina Lux holds a Ph.D. in Romance Languages from the University of Oregon, a Certificate in Conflict Resolution from Cornell, and Certificates in Conflict Analysis, Negotiation, and Mediating Violent Conflict from the US Institute of Peace. Her poetry on topics such as breast cancer and COVID-19 has appeared in venues ranging from *National Public Radio* to the *Merced County Times*. Her book of poetry, *War Bonds*, also addresses

PTSD—from WWI to wars in Iraq and Afghanistan (forthcoming from FlowerSong Press in 2023). Her co-authored article on how poetry can enhance innovation in conservation science was published in *BioScience* and her research on multilingual writers has appeared in the *Journal of Transnational American Studies* and the *International Journal of Francophone Studies*. She is Managing Director of the Center for the Humanities at UC Merced.

Ignacio López-Calvo is Presidential Chair in the Humanities, Director of the Center for the Humanities, and Professor of Literature at the University of California, Merced. He is the author of more than one hundred articles and book chapters, as well as nine single-authored books and seventeen essay collections. He is the co-executive director of the academic journal *Transmodernity: Journal of Peripheral Cultural Production of the Luso-Hispanic World*, the Palgrave-Macmillan Book Series "Historical and Cultural Interconnections between Latin America and Asia," and the Anthem Press book series "Anthem Studies in Latin American Literature and Culture Series." His latest books are *The Mexican Transpacific: Nikkei Writing, Visual Arts, Performance* (forthcoming); *Saudades of Japan and Brazil: Contested Modernities in Lusophone Nikkei Cultural Production* (2019); *Dragons in the Land of the Condor: Tusán Literature and Knowledge in Peru* (2014), and *The Affinity of the Eye: Writing Nikkei in Peru* (2013).

Contributing Authors

Michael Bakan is Professor of Ethnomusicology at Florida State University. He is the author of the books *Music and Autism: Speaking for Ourselves*, *World Music: Traditions and Transformations*, and *Music of Death and New Creation*. His work prioritizes re-presentation over representation, bringing the voices and ideas of autistic musicians to the foreground of collaborative ventures in research, social action, and creative musical endeavor. Bakan co-chairs the Music and Intercultural Diversity (MINd) Special Interest Group of the International Association for Music and Medicine (IAMM) and formerly served on the Board of Directors of the Society for Ethnomusicology (SEM), as president of the SEM Southeast/Caribbean Chapter, and on the Central Fellowships Committee of the American Council of Learned Societies. As a drummer and percussionist, he has performed with John Cage, George Clinton, Tito Puente, Pauline Oliveros, the Toronto Symphony Orchestra, the Los Angeles Philharmonic Green Umbrella Players, and leading gamelan ensembles in Bali, Indonesia. Recent recordings include *A History of the Future*, with Longineu Parsons and Brian Hall, and *Medicaid Fraud Dogg*, with the legendary funk band Parliament.

Yu-Han Chao was born and grew up in Taipei, Taiwan, received her BA from National Taiwan University, MFA from Pennsylvania State University, BSN from California State University, Stanislaus, and MSN from Purdue University Global. She taught at Merced College and the University of California, Merced, for over ten years and currently works as an Intensive Care Unit Registered Nurse. The University of Nebraska Press published her poetry book, *We Grow Old*, in 2008, and Dancing Girl Press, *Another New Calligraphy*; BOAAT Press published her chapbooks. Red Hen Press published her story collection, *Sex & Taipei City*, in 2019. Her poetry collection, *Six Degrees of Polypeptide*, is forthcoming with PANK. She maintains a blog about writing and health topics at www.yuhanchao.com.

Brian Dolan is Chair of the Department of Humanities and Social Sciences in the School of Medicine at UCSF and Professor of History of Health Sciences. His research areas include historical perspectives on the development of modern clinical practices and medical epistemology; the ethics and values of medical technologies, such as information management systems and telemedicine. In addition to his research on philosophical and medical perceptions of narrative, he is writing an introductory history of American health care costs. He edited *Humanitas: Readings in the Development of the Medical Humanities* (2015), which examines a century of efforts to integrate humanities subjects with medical education.

Dr. Yvette Flores is a community-clinical psychologist who obtained a doctoral degree in Clinical Psychology at U.C. Berkeley in 1982. She has done postdoctoral work in health psychology, and her research focus has been substance abuse treatment outcomes, women's mental health, intimate partner violence, the mental health of immigrant men, and Latina pathways to STEM careers. A Professor of Psychology in Chicana/o Studies at U.C. Davis for the past 32 years, Dr. Flores's publications reflect her life's work of bridging community and clinical psychology and Chicano/Latino studies as she foregrounds gender, ethnicity, and sexualities in her clinical, teaching and research practice. Her book *Chicana and Chicano Mental Health: Alma, Mente y Corazon* was published by the University of Arizona Press in March of 2013, and *Psychological Perspectives for Chicano/Latino Families* was published by Cognella Academic Publishers in 2014. Sentia Academic Publishers published *Psychological Perspectives on Latinx Children and Adolescents* in 2016. Her latest book, *Cultura y Corazón: A Decolonial Methodology for Community Engaged Research*, was published by the University of Arizona Press in 2020. Dr. Flores is a national and international consultant on cultural humility, prevention and treatment of trauma, gender, migration, mental health, and self-care for advocates of color.

Graeme Gibson is a multi-instrumentalist, composer, instrument builder, and online museum curator based in Vancouver, Canada.

Ithar Hassaballa, PhD, MPH, has a decade of experience in community-based participatory research and program evaluation in health equity and global health. She consulted for the World Health Organization's (WHO) African Regional Office (2011-2018) on health promotion, evaluation, training, and capacity-building needs. Additionally, she managed the evaluation, technical assistance, and consultation for the Bristol-Myers Squibb Foundation's Together on Diabetes Population Health cluster (2012-2017), which included six grantees that focused on various historically excluded populations (e.g., Black women) within 16 communities across the United States. She worked as Research Project Manager to address youth violence prevention among Black and Latino youth in Kansas City, Kansas. As the Research Project Director/Assistant Director at the University of Kansas' Center for Public Partnerships and Research, she led projects to understand and improve conditions for children and families to thrive in Kansas. She led a grant to support public health infrastructure building in 20 Kansas counties. She is currently Population Health Team Lead at the Kansas Health Institute where she leads a team that assists policy makers, stakeholders, and communities with advancing equitable policies and programs that aim to improve the health outcomes of populations.

Ruaa Hassaballa-Muhammad, MPH, is the Project Manager-Northeast Regional Community Lead for COPE (Communities Organizing to Promote Equity) and leads 5 Northeast Kansas counties to address social determinants of health impacting COVID-19 disparities. She previously served as the COVID Testing Equity Project Manager for Lawrence-Douglas County Public Health in Kansas, where she led surveillance testing efforts for all of Douglas County with an equity lens. Given her global leadership experience, she centers cultural humility in her approach to increasing equitable access to testing and vaccinations for historically marginalized and underserved populations. She served as a Global Health Council Delegate to the World Health Organization's Health Assembly in Geneva, Switzerland, in 2017. In addition to Switzerland, her reach to advance the impact of equity in the field of public health includes the United Kingdom, Sudan, Australia, and Kenya. Domestically, Ruaa has conducted presentations, research, and consultation across the United States from Seattle, Washington, to Atlanta, Georgia. Many of these experiences, along with earning a master's degree in public health focused on epidemiology, led to her current pursuit of a Ph.D. in Behavior Psychology with a concentration in Community Health and Development at the University of Kansas. She is a 2021 Next Generation Global Leader Fellow with the US Global Leadership Coalition.

Mariana Pascual is an Associate Professor in Discourse Studies at the Pontificia Universidad Católica de Chile. She holds a PhD in Linguistics (Universidad de Buenos Aires, Argentina) and an M.A. in English, Applied Linguistics. Her research interests include the construction of interpersonal meanings in scientific discourse, discourses of human rights, and media discourse. She has conducted research in English and in Spanish. Her current project, "Discourse and women's reproductive health," focuses on how Chilean women with chronic diseases construct their evaluations, feelings, and emotions across different discourse genres. The ultimate purpose of her research is to help them improve their communication and, consequently, their life quality. She has published extensively on the evaluative dimension of affect and how it is affected by sociocultural factors.

Bibliography

"Advance Health Care Directive Form," State of California Department of Justice. Accessed January 2019. https://oag.ca.gov/sites/all/files/agweb/pdfs/consumers/ProbateCodeAdvancedHealthCareDirective Form-fillable.pdf.

"Determination of Death," Uniform Determination of Death Act § 1 (2015).

African Health Action Toolkit. 2016. Accessed Feb. 7, 2023. https://who-afro.ctb.ku.edu/.

Alegría, Margarita, Norah Mulvaney-Day, Maria Torres, Antonio Polo, Zhun Cao, Glorisa Canino. 2007. "Prevalence of psychiatric disorders across Latino subgroups in the United States." *American Journal of Public Health* 97: 68–75.

Alvarado, Karina Oliva, Estrada, Alicia Ivonne, Ester E. Hernandez. 2017. *U.S. Central Americans: Reconstructing Memories, Struggles, and Communities of Resistance.* Tucson: University of Arizona Press.

American Psychiatric Association. 2013a. *Diagnostic and Statistical Manual of Mental Disorders: DSM-5.* 5th ed. Washington, D.C.: American Psychiatric Association.

American Psychiatric Association. 2013b. "Social (Pragmatic) Communication Disorder" [DSM-5 online fact sheet]. Washington, D.C.: American Psychiatric Association. Accessed October 14, 2022. https://www.psychiatry.org/File%20Library/Psychiatrists/Practice/DSM/APA_DSM-5-Social-Communication-Disorder.pdf.

American Public Health Association. 2020. "AHPA leader calls for greater access to COVID-19 resources for Hispanics." Accessed April 2021.

https://www.apha.org/news-and-media/news-releases/apha-news-releases/2020/hispanics-and-covid-19.

Anderson, Michael. 2013. "A Question of Location - Life with Fatigue After Stroke." University of Copenhagen.

Atkinson, Sarah, Bethan Evans, Angela Woods, and Robin Kearns. 2015. "'The Medical' and 'Health' in a Critical Medical Humanities." *Journal of Medical Humanities* 36, no. 1: 71-81. doi: 10.1007/s10912-014-9314-4.

Avineri, Netta, Laura R. Graham, Eric J. Johnson, Robin Conley Riner, and Jonathan Rosa. ed. 2019. Language and Social Justice in Practice. New York: Routledge.

Bakan, Michael B. 2015. "'Don't Go Changing to Try and Please Me': Combating Essentialism through Ethnography in the Ethnomusicology of Autism." *Ethnomusicology* 59, no. 1: 116–44.

Bakan, Michael B. 2016. "Music, Autism, and Disability Aesthetics." Colloquy: On the Disability Aesthetics of Music, convened by Blake Howe and Stephanie Jensen-Moulton. *Journal of the American Musicological Society* 69, no. 2: 548-53.

Bakan, Michael B. 2018. "Music and Autism, Representation and Re-presentation: An Ethnomusicological Perspective." In *Autism in Translation: An Intercultural Conversation on Autism Spectrum Conditions*, edited by Elizabeth Fein and Clarice Rios, 109-128. Cham, Switzerland: Palgrave Macmillan.

Bakan, Michael B., with Mara Chasar, Graeme Gibson, Elizabeth J. Grace, Zena Hamelson, Dotan Nitzberg, Gordon Peterson, Maureen Pytlik, Donald Rindale, Amy Sequenzia, and Addison Silar. 2018. *Speaking for Ourselves: Conversations on Life, Music, and Autism*. New York: Oxford University Press.

Bakan, Michael B., with Mara Chasar, Graeme Gibson, Elizabeth J. Grace, Zena Hamelson, Dotan Nitzberg, Gordon Peterson, Maureen

Pytlik, Donald Rindale, Amy Sequenzia, and Addison Silar. 2021. *Music and Autism: Speaking for Ourselves*. New York: Oxford University Press.

Bañón Hernández, Antonio Miguel. 2018. *Discurso y Salud. Análisis de un Debate Social*. Primera. Navarra: Ediciones Universidad de Navarra (EUNSA).

Betancourt, Hector, Patricia M. Flynn, and Sarah R. Ormseth. 2011. "Healthcare mistreatment and continuity of cancer screening among Latino and Anglo American women in Southern California." *Women & Health* 51, no. 1: 1-24.

Bonnin, Juan Eduardo. 2013. "The Public, the Private and the Intimate in Doctor-Patient Communication: Admission Interviews at an Outpatient Mental Health Care Service." *Discourse Studies* 15, no. 6: 687–711. https://doi.org/10.1177/1461445613492249.

Braghetto, Ítalo M., and Patricio Baronti. 2007. "Relación Paciente-Médico. Una Alianza Que Fomenta La Calidad* Relation Patient-Doctor and Quality of the Attention DOCUMENTOS." *Rev. Chilena de Cirugía* 59: 385–92.

Bryant-Davis, Thema, and Lillian Comas-Diaz. 2016. *Womanist and Mujerista Psychologies: Voices of Fire, Acts of Courage*. Washington: American Psychological Association.

Bukstein, Don A. 2016. "Patient Adherence and Effective Communication." *Annals of Allergy, Asthma & Immunology* 117, no. 6: 613–619. https://doi.org/10.1016/J.ANAI.2016.08.029.

Bullo, Stella, and Jasmine Heath Hearn. 2020. "Parallel Worlds and Personified Pain: A Mixed-Methods Analysis of Pain Metaphor Use by Women with Endometriosis." *British Journal of Health Psychology* 26, no. 2: 271–288. https://doi.org/10.1111/bjhp.12472.

Bullo, Stella. 2018. "Exploring Disempowerment in Women's Accounts of Endometriosis Experiences." *Discourse and Communication* 13, no. 6: 419–445. https://doi.org/10.1177/1750481318771430.

Bullo, Stella. 2019. "'I Feel like I'm Being Stabbed by a Thousand Tiny Men': The Challenges of Communicating Endometriosis Pain." *Health (United Kingdom)* 24, no. 5: 476–492. https://doi.org/10.1177/1363459318817943.

Center for Disease Control and Prevention. n.d. "Provisional Death Counts for Coronavirus Disease 2019." National Center for Health Statistics. Accessed January 27, 2023. https://www.cdc.gov/nchs/nvss/vsrr/covid19/index.htm.

Centers for Disease Control and Prevention. n.d. "Health Disparities: Race and Hispanic origin provisional death counts for coronavirus disease." National Center for Health Statistics. Accessed January 27, 2023. https://www.cdc.gov/nchs/nvss/vsrr/covid19/health_disparities.htm#RaceHispanicOrigin.

Centers for Disease Control and Prevention. n.d. COVID Data Tracker. Accessed January 27, 2023. https://covid.cdc.gov/covid-data-tracker/#datatracker-home.

Charmaz, Kathy. 1983. "Loss of Self: A Fundamental Form of Suffering in the Chronically Ill." *Sociology of Health & Illness* 5, no. 2: 168–95. https://doi.org/10.1111/1467-9566.ep10491512.

Charon, Rita, Sayantani DasGupta, Nellie Hermann, Craig Irvine, Eric Marcus, Edgar Rivera-Colon, Danielle Spencer, and Maura Spiegel. 2017. *The Principles and Practice of Narrative Medicine.* New York: Oxford University Press.

Cheng, Hsiu-Lan, Anna Lopez, Jamey L. Rislin, Helen Youngju Kim, Joshua Turner, Heather Terhorst-Miller, Jessica Lopez-Harder, and Chu Hui Cha. 2018. "Latino/Hispanic Community Adults' Healthcare Experience in a New Mexico Borderland Region." *Journal of Health Disparities Research and Practice* 11, no. 4, article 5. https://digitalscholarship.unlv.edu/jhdrp/vol11/iss4/5.

Cheston, Rik. 1996. "Stories and Metaphors: Talking about the Past in a

Psychotherapy Group for People with Dementia." *Ageing and Society* 16, no. 5: 579–602. https://doi.org/10.1017/S0144686X00020249

Chinman, Matthew, Gordon Hannah, Abraham Wandersman, Patricia Ebener, Sarah B. Hunter, Pamela Imm, Jeffrey Sheldon. 2005. "Developing a community science research agenda for building community capacity for effective preventive interventions." *American Journal of Community Psychology* 35, no. 3-4: 143-57.

Clarke, Adele and Joan Fujimura. 1992. *The Right Tools for the Job: At Work in Twentieth-Century Life Sciences*. Princeton: Princeton University Press.

Community Tool Box. n.d. Tools to change our world. Accessed Feb. 7, 2023. http://ctb.ku.edu/en.

Cousins, J. Bradly and Elizabeth Whitmore. 1998. "Framing participatory evaluation." *New Directions for Evaluation* 80: 5-23.

Crenshaw, Kimberlé W. 2017. *On Intersectionality: Essential Writings*. New York, NY: The New Press.

Creswell, John W., Vicki L. Plano-Clark, Michelle L. Gutmann, and William E. Hanson. 2003. "Advanced Mixed Methods Research Designs." In *Handbook of Mixed Methods in Social and Behavioral Research*, edited by Abbas Tashakkori, Charles Teddlie, and Charles B. Teddlie, 209–40. Thousand Oaks, CA: Sage.

Damasio, Antonio R., Ursula Bellugi, Hanna Damasio, Howard Poizner, and John Van Gilder. 1986. "Sign Language Aphasia during Left-Hemisphere Amytal Injection." *Nature* 322, no. 6077: 363–65. https://doi.org/10.1038/322363a0.

Danielou, Alain. 1968. *The Ragas of Northern Indian Music*. London: Barrie and Rockliff.

de la Torre, Adela, Banafsheh Sadeghi, Richard D. Green, Lucia L. Kaiser, Yvette G. Flores, Carlos F. Jackson, Sara E. Schaefer, Ulfat Shaikh, Linda Whent. 2013. "Niños Sanos, Familia Sana: Mexican Immigrant Study Protocol for a Multifaceted CBPR intervention to combat childhood obesity in two rural California towns." *BMC Public Health* 13, no. 1033. Doi:10.1186/1471-2458-13-1033, http://www.biomedcentral.com/1471-2458/13/1033.

Daston, Lorraine. 2008. "On Scientific Observation." *Isis* 99, no. 1: 97-110.

Deeb-Sossa, Natalia. ed. 2019. *Community-Based Participatory Research: Testimonios from Chicana/o Studies*. Tucson: University of Arizona Press.

Dolan, Brian. 2015. "One Hundred Years of Medical Humanities: A Thematic Overview." In *Humanitas: Readings in the Development of the Medical Humanities*, edited by Brian Dolan, 1–30. University of California Medical Humanities Press.

Dong, Jie. 2021. "Language and globalization revisited: Life from the periphery in COVID-19." *International Journal of the Sociology of Language*, no. 267-268: 105-110. https://doi.org/10.1515/ijsl-2020-0086.

Duffy, Robert J., Joseph R. Duffy, and Karen Leiter Pearson. 1975. "Pantomime Recognition in Aphasics." *Journal of Speech and Hearing Research* 18, no. 1: 115–32. https://doi.org/10.1044/jshr.1801.115.

Elliott, Carl, and Britt Elliott. 1991. "From the Patient's Point of View: Medical Ethics and the Moral Imagination." *Journal of Medical Ethics* 17, no. 4: 173–78. https://doi.org/10.1136/jme.17.4.173.

Ethan Kross, Emma Bruehlman-Senecal, Jiyoung Park, Aleah Burson, Adrienne Dougherty, Holly Shablack, Ryan Bremner, Jason Moser, and Ozlem Ayduk. 2014. "Self-Talk as a Regulatory Mechanism: How You Do It Matters." *Journal of Personality and Social Psychology* 106, no. 2: 304–24.

Eyster, Harold N., Terre Satterfield, and Kai M.A. Chan. 2022. "Why People Do What They Do: An Interdisciplinary Synthesis of Human Action Theories." *Annual Review of Environment and Resources* 47. https://doi.org/10.1146/annurev-environ-020422-125351.

Facchin, Federica, Giussy Barbara, Emanuela Saita, Paola Mosconi, Anna Roberto, Luigi Fedele, and Paolo Vercellini. 2015. "Impact of Endometriosis on Quality of Life and Mental Health: Pelvic Pain Makes the Difference." *Journal of Psychosomatic Obstetrics and Gynecology* 36, no. 4: 135–141. https://doi.org/10.3109/016748 2X.2015.1074173.

Fauconnier, Arnaud, Hocine Drioueche, Cyrille Huchon, Joseph du Cheyron, Emilie Indersie, Yasmine Candau, Pierre Panel, and Xavier Fritel. 2021. "Early Identification of Women with Endometriosis by Means of a Simple Patient-Completed Questionnaire Screening Tool: A Diagnostic Study." *Fertility and Sterility* 116, no. 6: 1580–1589. https://doi.org/10.1016/j.fertnstert.2021.07.1205.

Fawcett, Stephen B., Renée Boothroyd, Jerry A. Schultz, Vincent T. Francisco, Valorie Carson, and Roderick Bremby. 2003. "Building Capacity for Participatory Evaluation Within Community Initiatives." *Journal of Prevention & Intervention in the Community* 26, no. 2: 21-36.

Fawcett, Stephen B., Vincent T. Francisco, Jerry A. Schultz, Bill Berkowitz, Thomas J. Wolff, and Genevieve Nagy. 2000. "The Community Tool Box: A Web-based resource for building healthier communities." *Public Health Reports* 115: 274–78.

Fawcett, Stephen B., Vincent T. Francisco, Jerry A. Schultz. 2004. "Understanding and Improving the Work of Community Health and Development." In *Theory, basic and applied research, and technological applications in behavior science*, edited by Jose Burgos and Emilio Ribes, 209-42. Guadalajara, Mexico: Universidad de Guadalajara.

Fawcett, Stephen B., Jerry A. Schultz, Vincent Thomas Francisco, Bill Berkowitz, Thomas J. Wolff, Paul W. Rabinotitz, Christina Marie Holt, Jami A. Jones. 2008. "Using Internet technology for capacity development in communities: The case of   the Community Tool Box." In *Strategies of Community Intervention*, edited by Jack Rothman,

John L. Erlich, and John E. Tropman, 7th ed. 263–281. Peosta, IA: Eddie Bowers Publishing Co.

Fawcett, Steven B., Theodore D. Sterling, K. J. Harris, and Adrienne Paine-Andrews. 1998. *Evaluating Community Efforts To Prevent Cardiovascular Disease.* Collingdale, PA; Diane Publishing Co.

Fawcett, Steven, Palitha Abeykoon, Monica Arora, Madhumita Dobe, Lark Galloway-Gilliam, Leandris Liburd, and Davison Munodawafa. 2010. "Constructing an action agenda for community empowerment at the 7th Global Conference on Health Promotion in Nairobi." *Global Health Promotion* 17, no. 4: 52-56.

Fein, Elizabeth, and Clarice Rios, ed. 2018. *Autism in Translation: An Intercultural Conversation on Autism Spectrum Conditions.* Cham, Switzerland: Palgrave Macmillan.

Finocchario-Kessler, Sarah, Brad J. Gautney, Samoel Khamadi, Vincent Okoth, Kathy Goggin, Jennifer K. Spinler, Anne Mwangi et al. 2014. "If you text them, they will come: using the HIV infant tracking system to improve early infant diagnosis quality and retention in Kenya." *AIDS (London, England)* 28, no. 3: 313.

Fitzgerald, Des and Felicity Callard. 2016. "Entangling the Medical Humanities." In *The Edinburgh Companion to the Critical Medical Humanities,* edited by *Anne Whitehead and Angela Woods, 35-49.* Edinburgh: Edinburgh University Press.

Flores, Yvette G. 2013. *Chicana and Chicano Mental Health: Alma, Mente y Corazón (The Mexican Experience).* Tucson: University of Arizona Press.

Flores, Yvette G. 2022. "Finding Home / Haciendo Familia: Testimonios of Mexican Male Farmworkers in Central California." In *Latinx Belonging: Community Building and Resilience in the United States,* edited by Natalia Deeb-Sosa and Jennifer Bickham Mendez, 143-65. Tucson: University of Arizona Press.

Flores, Yvette G., Lisceth Brazil-Cruz, Hector Rivera-Lopez, Rosa D.

Manzo, Monica Siañez, and Erika I. Cervantes-Pacheco. 2019. "Aquí en Confianza (Here in Confidence): Narratives of Migration, Mental Health, and Family Reunification of Mexican Immigrant Men in the California Central Valley." In *Community-Based Participatory Research: Testimonios from Chicana/o Studies*, edited by Natalia Deeb-Sossa, 153-78. Tucson: University of Arizona Press.

Francisco, Vincent T., Adrienne L. Paine, and Stephen B. Fawcett. 1993. "A methodology for monitoring and evaluating community health coalitions." *Health Education Research* 8, no. 3: 403-16.

Gallagher, Shaun. 2000. "Philosophical Conceptions of the Self: Implications for Cognitive Science." *Trends in Cognitive Sciences* 4, no. 1: 14–21. https://doi.org/10.1016/S1364-6613(99)01417-5

Geva, Sharon, Sophie Bennett, Elizabeth A. Warburton, and Karalyn Patterson. 2011. "Discrepancy between Inner and Overt Speech: Implications for Post-Stroke Aphasia and Normal Language Processing." *Aphasiology* 25, no. 3: 323–343. https://doi.org/10.1080/02687038.2010.511236.

Gibson, Deborah. 2011. "The Early Lexical Acquisition of a Child with Autism Spectrum Disorder." Doctoral Dissertation (Language and Literacy Education), University of British Columbia.

Gibson, Graeme. "Museum of World Music." Accessed March 15, 2022. museumofworldmusic.com.

Gibson, William. 1984. *Neuromancer*. New York: Ace Books.

Goldstein, Kurt. 1940. *Human Nature in the Light of Psychopathology: The William James Lecture*. Cambridge, MA: Harvard University Press.

Gonzalez, Elsa. 2020. "Foreword: understanding Latina/o resilience." *International Journal of Qualitative Studies in Education* 33, no.8: 791-95.

Graham, Jeremy, Lauren M. Benson, Judy Swanson, Darryl Potyk, Kenn Daratha, and Ken Roberts. 2016. "Medical Humanities Coursework Is Associated with Greater Measured Empathy in Medical Students."

The American Journal of Medicine 129, no.12: 1334-1337.

Halliday, Michael A. K. 1978. *Language as Social Semiotic. The Discourse Studies Reader: Main Currents in Theory and Analysis.* London: Edward Arnold. https://doi.org/10.1075/z.184.53hal.

Halliday, Michael A. K. 2004. *An Introduction to Functional Grammar*, revised by Cristian M.I.M. Matthiessen. 3rd ed. London: Routledge. https://doi.org/10.4324/9780203783771.

Hållstam, Andrea, Britt-Marie Stålnacke, Christer Svensén, and Monika Löfgren. 2018. "Living with Painful Endometriosis – A Struggle for Coherence. A Qualitative Study." *Sexual & Reproductive Healthcare* 17 (October): 97–102. https://doi.org/10.1016/J.SRHC.2018.06.002.

Harvey, Kevin, and Nelya Koteyko. 2012. "Patients' Narratives of Health and Illness." In *Exploring Health Communication: Language in Action*, edited by Kevin Harvey and Nelya Koteyko, 70–92. London & New York: Routledge. https://doi.org/10.4324/9780203096437-11.

Hassaballa, Ithar, Fawcett, Stephen, Sepers Jr., Charles, et al. 2019. "Participatory monitoring and evaluation of Ebola response activities in Lofa County, Liberia: Some lessons learned." *International Quarterly of Community Health Education* 40, no 1: p. 57-66.

Henderson, Victor W. 1990. "Alalia, Aphemia, and Aphasia." *Archives of Neurology (Chicago)* 47, no. 1: 85–88. https://doi.org/10.1001/archneur.1990.00530010107028

Hennegan, Julie, Inga T. Winkler, Chris Bobel, Danielle Keiser, Janie Hampton, Gerda Larsson, Venkatraman Chandra-Mouli, Marina Plesons, and Thérèse Mahon. 2021. "Menstrual Health: A Definition for Policy, Practice, and Research." *Sexual and Reproductive Health Matters* 29, no. 1: 31–38. https://doi.org/10.1080/26410397.2021.1911618.

Hinojosa, Ramon, Craig Boylstein, Maude Rittman, Melanie Sberna Hinojosa, and Christopher A. Faircloth. 2008. "Constructions of Continuity after Stroke." *Symbolic Interaction* 31, no. 2: 205–24. https://

doi.org/10.1525/si.2008.31.2.205

Hojat, Mohammadreza, Daniel Z. Louis, Fred W. Markham, Richard Wender, Carol Rabinowitz, and Joseph S. Gonnella. 2011. "Physicians' empathy and clinical outcomes for diabetic patients." *Academic medicine: journal of the Association of American Medical Colleges* 86, no.3: 359–364. https://doi.org/10.1097/ACM.0b013e3182086fe1.

HRSA organdonor.gov "Organ Donation Statistics," Health Resources and Services Administration. Accessed March 2022. https://www. organdonor.gov/learn/organ-donation-statistics.

Hudelist, Gernot, Nadya Fritzer, Almut Thomas, Christiane Niehues, Peter Oppelt, Dietmar

Haas, Ayman Tammaa, and Heinrich Salzer. 2012. "Diagnostic Delay for Endometriosis in Austria and Germany: Causes and Possible Consequences." *Human Reproduction* 27, no. 12: 3412–3416. https:// doi.org/10.1093/HUMREP/DES316.

IASP. 1979. "Pain terms: a list with definitions and notes on usage: recommended by the IASP Subcommittee on Taxonomy." *Pain* 6, no. 3: 249.

Ignatavicius, Donna D., and M. Linda Workman. 2013. *Medical-Surgical Nursing: Patient-Centered Collaborative Care.* 8th ed. St Louis, Missouri: Elsevier Saunders.

Iniewicz, Grzegorz, K. Salapa, Malgorzata Wrona, Natalia Marek. 2017. "Minority stress among homosexual and bisexual individuals - from theoretical concepts to research tools: The Sexual Minority Stress Scale." *Archives of Psychiatry and Psychotherapy* 3: 69–80.

Jackson, John Hughlings. 1915. "On The Nature Of The Duality Of The Brain." *Brain (London, England: 1878)* 38, no. 1–2: 80–86. https://doi. org/10.1093/brain/38.1-2.80.

Jacyna, L.S. 2009. *Lost Words: Narratives of Language and the Brain, 1825-1926.* Princeton: Princeton University Press.

Jia, Lile, Edward R. Hirt, and Samuel C. Karpen. 2009. "Lessons from a Faraway Land: The Effect of Spatial Distance on Creative Cognition." *Journal of Experimental Social Psychology* 45, no. 5: 1127-1131.

Juckett, Gregory. 2013. "Caring for Latino patients." *American Family Physician* 87, no.1: 48–54.

Kaufman, Sharon R. 2017. "'Losing My Self': A Poet's Ironies and a Daughter's Reflections on Dementia." *Perspectives in Biology and Medicine* 60, no. 4: 549–68. https://doi.org/10.1353/pbm.2017.0042.

Kaufman, Sharon. 1988. "Illness, Biography, and the Interpretation of Self Following a Stroke." *Journal of Aging Studies* 2, no. 3: 217–27. https://doi.org/10.1016/0890-4065(88)90002-3

Klugman, Craig M. 2017. "How Health Humanities Will Save the Life of the Humanities." *The Journal of Medical Humanities* 38, no. 4: 419-430.

Koller, Veronika, and Stella Bullo. 2019. "'Fight Like a Girl': Tattoos as Identity Constructions for Women Living with Illness." *Multimodal Communication* 8, no. 1: 20180006. https://doi.org/10.1515/mc-2018-0006.

Krogstad, Jens Manuel, Ana Gonzalez-Barrera, and Mark Hugo Lopez. 2020. "Hispanics more likely than Americans overall to see coronavirus as a major threat to health and finances." Pew Research Center. Accessed April 20, 2021.https://www.pewresearch.org/fact-tank/2020/03/24/hispanics-more-likely-than-americans-overall-to-see-coronavirus-as-a-major-threat-to-health-and-finances/.

Kuzmina, Ekaterina, Mira Goral, Monica Norvik, and Brendan S. Weekes. 2019. "What Influences Language Impairment in Bilingual Aphasia? A Meta-Analytic Review." *Frontiers in Psychology* 10. https://doi.org/10.3389/fpsyg.2019.00445.

Laganà, Antonio Simone, Valentina Lucia la Rosa, Agnese Maria Chiara Rapisarda, Gaetano Valenti, Fabrizio Sapia, Benito Chiofalo, Diego

Rossetti, Helena Ban Frangež, Eda Vrtačnik Bokal, and Salvatore Giovanni Vitale. 2017. "Anxiety and Depression in Patients with Endometriosis: Impact and Management Challenges." *International Journal of Women's Health* 9: 323–330. https://doi.org/10.2147/IJWH. S119729.

Laster Pirtle, Whitney N. 2020. "Racial Capitalism: A Fundamental Cause of Novel Coronavirus (COVID-19) Pandemic Inequities in the United States." *Health Education & Behavior* 47, no. 4: 504-508.

Laster Pirtle, Whitney N., and Tashelle Wright. 2021. "Structural Gendered Racism Revealed in Pandemic Times: Intersectional Approaches to Understanding Race and Gender Health Inequities in COVID-19." *Gender & Society* 35, no. 2: 168-179.

Leung, Margaret W., Irene H. Yen, and Meredith Minkler. 2004. "Community based participatory research: a promising approach for increasing epidemiology's relevance in the 21st century." *International Journal of Epidemiology* 33, no. 3: 499-506.

Lordat, Jacques. 1843. "Analyse de la parole pour servir à la théorie de divers cas d'ALALIE et de PARALALIE (de mutisme et d'imperfection du parler) que les Nosologistes ont mal connus." *Journal de la Société de Médecine Pratique de Montpellier* 7: 417-433.

Magaña, Dalia. 2020. "Local Voices on Healthcare Communication Issues and Insights on Latino Cultural Constructs." *Hispanic Journal of Behavioral Sciences* 42, no. 3: 300–323.

Magaña, Dalia. 2021. *Building confianza: Empowering Latinos/as through transcultural health care communication.* The Ohio State University Press.

Mangione, Salvatore, Chayan Chakraborti, Giuseppe Staltari, Rebecca Harrison, Allan R. Tunkel, Kevin T. Liou, Elizabeth Cerceo, Megan Voeller, Wendy L. Bedwell, Keaton Fletcher, and Marc J. Kahn. 2018. "Medical Students' Exposure to the Humanities Correlates with Positive Personal Qualities and Reduced Burnout: A Multi-Institutional U.S. Survey." *Journal of General Internal Medicine* 33, no. 5: 628–634.

Manzo, Rosa D., Lisceth Brazil-Cruz, Yvette G. Flores, and Hector Rivera-Lopez. 2020. *Cultura y Corazón: A Decolonial Methodology for Community Engaged Research.* Tucson: The University of Arizona Press.

Markides, Kyriakos S., and Jeannine Coreil. 1986. "The Health of Hispanics in the Southwestern United States: an Epidemiological Paradox." *Public Health Reports,* no.101: 253-65.

Marmot, Michael. 2005. "Social determinants of health inequalities." *The Lancet* 365, no. 9464: 1099-1104.

Marmot, Michael. 2005. *Status Syndrome: How Your Social Standing Directly Affects Your Health.* London: Bloomsbury Publishing.

Martín-Baró, Ignacio. 1994. *Writings for a Liberation Psychology.* Cambridge: Harvard University Press.

Martin, James R. 1985. "Process and Text: Two Aspects of Human Semiosis." In *Systemic Perspectives on Discourse.*, edited by James Benson and William Greave, 1: 248–274. Norwood, NJ: Praeger.

Martin, James R. 2000. "Beyond Exchange: Appraisal Systems in English." In *Evaluation in Text: Authorial Stance and the Construction of Discourse,* edited by Susan Hunston and Geoff Thompson, 142–175. Oxford: Oxford University Press.

Martin, James R. 2009. "Genre and Language Learning: A Social Semiotic Perspective." *Linguistics and Education* 20, no. 1: 10–21. https://doi.org/10.1016/j.linged.2009.01.003.

Martin, James R., and David Rose. 2007. *Working with Discourse: Meaning beyond the Clause.* London: Continuum.

Martin, James R., and Peter R.R. White. 2005. *The Language of Evaluation: Appraisal in English.* London: Palgrave Macmillan. https://doi.org/10.1057/9780230511910.

McCormack, Josh. 2021. "Study: Latinos Suffered Highest Rate of COVID-19 Hospitalizations." Salud America!. Accessed January 27, 2023. https://salud-america.org/study-latinos-suffered-highest-rate-of-covid-19-hospitalizations/.

McKnight-Eily, Lela R., Cathrine A. Okoro, Tara W. Strine, Jorge Verlenden, NaTasha D. Hollis, Rashid Naji, Elizabeth W. Michell, Amy Board, Richard Puddy, and Craig Thomas. 2021. "Racial and Ethnic Disparities in the Prevalence of Stress and Worry, Mental Health Conditions, and Increased Substance Use Among Adults During the COVID-19 Pandemic — United States, April and May 2020." Accessed January 23, 2023. *MMWR Morbidity and mortality weekly report* 70 (5):162–66. doi:10.15585/mmwr.mm7005a3.

Merced County Department of Public Health. 2016. *Merced County: 2016 Community Health Assessment.* Accessed June 2022. https://www.countyofmerced.com/DocumentCenter/View/12213/CHA-FINAL---V1?bidId=.

Meyer, Ilan H. 2003. "Prejudice, Social Stress, and Mental Health in Lesbian, Gay, and Bisexual populations: Conceptual Issues and Research Evidence. *Psychological Bulletin 129*(5): 674-97. https://doi.org/10.1037/0033-2909.129.5.674.

Mills, Charles K. 1904. "Treatment Of Aphasia By Training." *Journal of the American Medical Association* XLIII, no. 26: 1940–1949. https://doi.org/10.1001/jama.1904.92500260002d.

Morgan, Alisa, and Nancy Helm-Estabrooks. 1987. "Back to the Drawing Board: A Treatment Program for Nonverbal Aphasic Patients." *Clinical Aphasiology* 17: 64–72.

Morin, Rich. 2013. "The most (and least) culturally diverse countries in the world." Accessed Feb. 7, 2023. https://www.pewresearch.org/fact-tank/2013/07/18/the-most-and-least-culturally-diverse-countries-in-the-world/.

Moser, Jason S., Adrienne Dougherty, Whitney I. Mattson, Benjamin
    Katz, Tim P. Moran, Darwin Guevarra, Holly Shablack, Ozlem
    Ayduk, John Jonides, Marc G. Berman, and Ethan Kross. 2017.
    "Third-Person Self-Talk Facilitates Emotion Regulation without
    Engaging Cognitive Control: Converging Evidence from ERP
    and FMRI." *Scientific Reports* 7, no. 1, article. 4519. https://doi.
    org/10.1038/s41598-017-04047-3.

Moss, C. Scott. 1972. *Recovery with Aphasia: The Aftermath of My Stroke.*
    Champaign, IL: University of Illinois Press.

Munodawafa, Davison, Moeti, Matshidiso Rebecca, PHORI, Peter
    Malekele, et al. 2018. "Monitoring and evaluating the Ebola response
    effort in two Liberian communities." *Journal of Community Health* 43, no
    2: 321-27.

Nakano, Erline. 2005. "Changes in the Perception and Sense of Self of
    Individuals With Aphasia: An Ethnographic Study." M.S. Thesis,
    University of South Florida. https://digitalcommons.usf.edu/
    etd/785/.

Ndugga, Nambi, Latoya Hill, Samantha Artiga, and Sweta Haldar. 2022.
    "Latest Data on COVID-19 Vaccination by race/ethnicity." Kaiser
    Family Foundation. Accessed January 27, 2023. https://www.kff.org/
    coronavirus-covid-19/issue-brief/latest-data-on-covid-19-vaccinations-
    by-race-ethnicity/.

Nettl, Bruno. 2005. *The Study of Ethnomusicology: Thirty-One Issues and
    Concepts.* New Edition (2nd). Urbana: University of Illinois Press.

Ngo, Thu, and Len Unsworth. 2015. "Reworking the Appraisal
    Framework in ESL Research: Refining Attitude Resources." *Functional
    Linguistics* 2, no. 1: 1–24. https://doi.org/10.1186/s40554-015-
    0013-x.

Nitzberg, Dotan, and Michael B. Bakan. 2019. "Resilience and Adaptive
    Management in Piano Pedagogy for Individuals on the Autism

Spectrum." In *Cultural Sustainabilities: Music, Media, Language, Advocacy*, edited by Timothy J. Cooley, 249-61. Urbana and Chicago: University of Illinois Press.

Office of Minority Health [OMH] 2021. The Impact of COVID-19 in Latinos: What can we do to move forward? Accessed November 30, 2021. Minorityhealth.hss.gov.

Okeyo, S. M., A. K. Karani, and E. Matheka. 2017. "Challenges of technological trends in nursing and coping strategies by nurses at Kenyatta National Hospital." *East African Medical Journal* 94, no. 11: 960-71.

Pascual, Mariana, and Natalia Díaz Alegría. 2021. "El Afecto en Relatos de Dolor Crónico en Comentarios de Facebook de Mujeres Chilenas." *Nueva Revista Del Pacífico*, no. 74: 47–63. https://doi.org/10.4067/s0719-51762021000100047.

Pascual, Mariana. 2020. "Discurso, Salud e Información desde el Relato de Pacientes de Endometriosis." *Discurso & Sociedad* 14, 2: 421–442. http://www.dissoc.org/ediciones/v14n02/DS14%282%29Pascual.pdf.

Pascual, Mariana. 2021. "Online Emotional Support: Discourse Functionalities on Chilean Facebook Pages by Patients with Chronic Pain." *Entrepalavras* 11, no. 3: 1–19. https://doi.org/10.22168/2237-6321-32298.

Pedersen, Reidar. 2010. "Empathy development in medical education - A critical review." *Medical Teacher* 32, no. 7: 593-600.

Penn, Claire, Tali Frankel, Jennifer Watermeyer, and Madeleine Müller. 2009. "Informed Consent and Aphasia: Evidence of Pitfalls in the Process." *Aphasiology* 23, no. 1: 3–32. https://doi.org/10.1080/02687030701521786.

Phori, Peter Malekele, Stephen Fawcett, Noemie Nikiema Nidjergou, Cleph Silouakadila, Ruaa Hassaballa, and Deogratias Kakule

Siku. "Participatory Monitoring and Evaluation of the COVID-19 Response in the Africa Region." Health Promotion Practice (2022): 15248399221095524.

Re-presentation: An Ethnomusicological Perspective' by Michael B. Bakan." Discussant remarks presented at Autism Spectrum Disorders in Global, Local and Personal Perspective: A Cross-Cultural Workshop, Rio De Janeiro, Brazil, September 2015.

Riese, Walther, and Judd Hubert. 1954. "Auto-Observation of Aphasia: Reported by an Eminent Nineteenth Century Medical Scientist." *Bulletin of the History of Medicine* 28, no. 3: 237–42.

Ross Decamp. 2016. "The "Battle" of Managing Language Barriers in Health Care." *Clinical Pediatrics* 55, no. 14: 1318–1327. https://doi.org/10.1177/0009922816629760.

Rubinsky, Valerie, Jacqueline N. Gunning, and Angela Cooke-Jackson. 2018. "'I Thought I Was Dying:' (Un)Supportive Communication Surrounding Early Menstruation Experiences." *Health Communication* 35, no. 2: 242–52. https://doi.org/10.1080/10410236.2018.1548337.

Sabat, Steven R., and Rom Harré. 1992. "The Construction and Deconstruction of Self in Alzheimer's Disease." *Ageing and Society* 12, no. 4: 443–61. https://doi.org/10.1017/S0144686X00005262.

Sánchez González, Miguel Ángel. 2017. "El Humanismo y la Enseñanza de las Humanidades Médicas." *Educación Médica* 18, no. 3: 212–218. https://doi.org/10.1016/j.edumed.2017.03.001.

Secretaria of the Interior/National Population Council (CONAPO), 2017. *Migration & Health: Reflections and challenges about the health of migrants.* Accessed January 27, 2023. https://www.gob.mx/conapo/archivo/documentos?idiom=es.

Sepers Jr, Charles E., Fawcett, Stephen B., Hassaballa, Ithar, et al. 2019. "Evaluating implementation of the Ebola response in Margibi County, Liberia." *Health Promotion International* 34, no 3: 510-18.

Shahin, Wejdan, Gerard A. Kennedy, and Ieva Stupans. 2019. "The Impact of Personal and Cultural Beliefs on Medication Adherence of Patients with Chronic Illnesses: A Systematic Review." *Patient Preference and Adherence* 13: 1019–1035. https://doi.org/10.2147/PPA.S212046.

Shapiro, Johanna, Jack Coulehan, Delese Wear, and Martha Montello. 2009. "Medical Humanities and Their Discontents: Definitions, Critiques, and Implications." *Academic Medicine* 84, no. 2: 192-198.

Simon, Sarah. 2021. "CDC: Latinx Community Hit Hard by COVID Mental Health Issues." *Very well health.* Accessed January 27, 2023. https://www.verywellhealth.com/latinx-mental-health-issues-cdc-report-5185748.

Smith, Ben J., Kwok Cho Tang, and Don Nutbeam. 2006. "WHO Health Promotion Glossary: new terms." *Health Promotion International* 21, no. 4: 340-45.

Smith, R. 1992. *Inhibition: History and Meaning in the Sciences of Mind and Brain.* Berkeley, CA: University of California Press.

Stæhr, Andreas. 2015. "Reflexivity in Facebook Interaction - Enregisterment across Written and Spoken Language Practices." *Discourse, Context and Media* 8: 30–45. https://doi.org/10.1016/j.dcm.2015.05.004.

Stubbe, Dorothy E. 2020. "Practicing Cultural Competence and Cultural Humility in the Care of Diverse Patients." *Focus* 18, no. 1: 49-51.

Tanner, Dennis C., and Dean L. Gerstenberger. 1988. "The Grief Response in Neuropathologies of Speech and Language." *Aphasiology* 2, no. 1: 79–84. https://doi.org/10.1080/02687038808248889

Taylor, Jill Bolte. 2008. *My Stroke of Insight: A Brain Scientist's Personal Journey.* New York, NY: Viking Press.

Teddlie, Charles, and Abbas Tashakkori. 2011. "Mixed Methods Research: Contemporary Issues in an Emerging Field." In *The SAGE Handbook of Qualitative Research,* edited by Norman K. Denzin and Yvonna S. Lincoln, 285–300. Thousand Oaks, CA: SAGE Publications, Inc.

Tervalon, Melanie, and J Murray-Garcia. 1998. "Cultural Humility Versus Cultural Competence: A Critical Distinction in Defining Physician Training Outcomes in Multicultural Education." *Journal of health care for the poor and underserved* 9(2): 117-25.

U.S. Census Bureau. 2018. *Quickfacts.* Accessed May 2021. https://www.census.gov/quickfacts/fact/.

Viney, William, Felicity Callard, and Angela Woods. 2015. "Critical medical humanities: embracing entanglement, taking risks." *Medical Humanities* 41, no. 1: 2-7.

Vallerstein, Nina, Bonnie Duran, John Oetzel, and Meredith Minkler. 2017. *Community-Based Participatory Research for Health: Advancing Social and Health Equity.* 3rd ed. San Francisco: Jossey-Bass (A Wiley Brand).

WHO Regional Office for Africa. 2022. Accessed Feb. 7, 2023. https://www.afro.who.int/

Wilkinson, Richard G., and Michael Marmot. 2003. *Social determinants of health: The solid facts.* World Health Organization.

Wodak, Ruth. 1997. "Critical Discourse Analysis and the Study of Doctor-Patient Interaction." In *The Construction of Professional Discourse,* edited by Britt-Louise Gunnarsson, Per Linell, and Bengt Nordberg, 173–200 London: Routledge.

World Health Organization Collaborating Centre for Community Health and Development. Accessed Feb. 7, 2023. https://communityhealth.ku.edu/who-collaborating-centre.

World Health Organization: Regional Office for Africa. 2013. Health Promotion Strategy for the African Region. Accessed Feb. 7, 2023. https://www.afro.who.int/sites/default/files/2017-06/Health%20Promotion%20Strategy%20inside%20English.pdf.

World Health Organization: Regional Office for Africa. 2014. The health

of the people, what works: The African Regional Health
Report 2014. Accessed Feb. 7, 2023. http://apps.who.int/iris/
bitstream/10665/137377/4/9789290232612.pdf.

Yeager, Katherine A. and Susan Bauer-Wu. 2013. "Cultural humility:
Essential foundation for clinical researchers." *Applied Nursing* 26 no. 4:
1-12.

Yosso, Tara J. 2006. "Whose culture has capital? A critical race theory
discussion of community cultural wealth." *Race Ethnicity and
Education* 8(1): 69-91. DOI: 10.1080/1361332052000341006.

Zamudio, Cindy D., Gabriela Sanchez, Andrea Altschuler, and Richard
W. Grant. 2017. "Influence of Language and Culture in the Primary
Care of Spanish-Speaking Latino Adults with Poorly Controlled
Diabetes: A Qualitative Study. *Ethnicity & Disease* 27, no. 4: 379–386.

Made in the USA
Monee, IL
18 February 2024

53720734R00116